RITUAL VESSELS OF BRONZE AGE CHINA

RITUAL VESSELS
OF
BRONZE AGE
CHINA

MAX LOEHR

THE ASIA SOCIETY INC. · DISTRIBUTED BY NEW YORK GRAPHIC SOCIETY LTD.

RITUAL VESSELS OF BRONZE AGE CHINA
is the catalogue of an exhibition selected by Dr. Max Loehr,
Abby Aldrich Rockefeller Professor of Oriental Art, Harvard University,
and shown in the Asia House Gallery in the fall of 1968
as an activity of The Asia Society,
to further greater understanding between
the United States and the peoples of Asia.

An Asia House Gallery Publication
Copyright 1968 by The Asia Society, Inc.
Printed in the United States of America
Library of Congress Catalogue Card Number: 68–30798

CONTENTS

FOREWORD

The Asia House Gallery of The Asia Society is honored to present this survey of notable bronzes from the Shang and Chou periods of ancient China, made available through the generosity of lenders in many parts of the world. They have been selected and catalogued by the distinguished scholar, Professor Max Loehr, who holds the chair of Abby Aldrich Rockefeller Professor of Oriental Art at Harvard University. Dr. Loehr's creative scholarship in this field has long been recognized throughout the world. His own eminent teacher, Dr. Ludwig Bachhofer, had already praised his work in the 1930's, recognizing his remarkable ability in establishing a dependable chronology for bronzes even when proof through inscriptions was not obtainable.

Subsequently, Professor Loehr published his epoch-making study of "The Bronze Styles of the Anyang Period (1300–1028 B.C.)" wherein he placed a series of Shang vessels in a chronology that archaeological excavations have since proven to be valid. By that study, he separated bronzes of the Anyang period into five distinct styles, making it possible for other scholars to refer to these Shang types by Roman numerals when cataloguing bronzes of this era.

Writing in *Artibus Asiae* (Vol. XXVII [1966]) in a critique of Dr. Loehr's article "Shang Bronze Styles," Professor Alexander C. Soper wrote: "The virtuosity of Loehr's analysis was supported, when he wrote, by theory alone; and the problem was so complex that it was possible for an unsympathetic reader to dismiss the whole construction if he disagreed with its first premise. The Honan reports have changed all of this. Re-studied in their brighter light, Loehr's two earliest styles are seen as an astonishing anticipation of what the next few years were to reveal in Middle Shang tombs. The vessel forms and most of the ornamental motifs that he selected from the enormous confusion of known bronze holdings, check perfectly with the new Chinese evidence. The accumulated weight of archaeological data[2] makes it far more certain than before that the I and II phases are not merely interesting and authentic but show the closest view we have as yet of the beginnings of the bronze vessel art in China."

Here, in this introduction to his catalogue, Dr. Loehr again offers a novel and stimulating contribution to the study of Chinese bronzes—a theory regarding the origin and significance of their décor or ornament. To conclude, as he does, that "most of the decorative designs on Shang and Chou bronzes may be characterized as purely ornamental" is to shatter previous interpretations. The moment there occurred a clear move towards reality, as in Han design, the age of bronzes was over, Dr. Loehr declares. As soon as real action was depicted, formal art was doomed.

The zoomorphic motifs that were used in conjunction with abstract motifs were, he notes, a Shang innovation, the abstract ones having already been developed in the decoration of Neolithic pottery. He concludes that the zoomorphic motifs actually developed out of the abstract motifs, as in the case of the well-known dragons on Late Shang bronzes. If this is the case, the zoomorphic motifs "cannot have had any ascertainable meaning—religious, cosmological or mythological—meaning, at any rate, of an established, literary kind." So, it is his conclusion that the non-realistic zoomorphs are merely design and "interesting solely on formal grounds, as 'pure art.'"

Clearly a landmark, this book, which also serves as a catalogue of the present exhibition, traces the new road that Dr. Loehr has blazed through a wilderness of beautiful relics. It is in itself an education to read the careful descriptions of each vessel that he has prepared, allowing one's eye to shift to the ritual bronze or to its photographic image for confirmation. These are among the greatest of man's inventions of any time or any place. Their mystery and their monumentality, as extensions of man, place them, as Dr. Loehr himself has once remarked, somewhere between pottery and architecture.

Gordon Bailey Washburn
Director, Asia House Gallery

---

1. *Archives of the Chinese Art Society of America* VII (1953), pp. 42-53
2. from excavations at Cheng-chou and Hui-hsien

LENDERS

The Ashmolean Museum, Oxford
Museum of Fine Arts, Boston
Mr. and Mrs. A. B. Martin (Guennol Collection), Courtesy of The Brooklyn Museum
Avery Brundage Collection, M. H. de Young Memorial Museum, San Francisco
Albright-Knox Art Gallery, Buffalo
Musée Cernuschi, Paris
Cincinnati Art Museum
The Art Institute of Chicago
The Cleveland Museum of Art
Museum für Ostasiatische Kunst, Cologne
Kunstindustrimuseum, Copenhagen
Mr. John M. Crawford, Jr., New York City
The Detroit Institute of Arts
Mr. and Mrs. Myron S. Falk, Jr., New York City
Fogg Art Museum, Harvard University, Cambridge, Mass.
Musée Guimet, Paris
Museum für Kunst und Gewerbe, Hamburg
Honolulu Academy of Arts
Mr. and Mrs. Frederick M. Mayer, New York City
The Metropolitan Museum of Art, New York City
The Minneapolis Institute of Arts
Mr. and Mrs. Earl Morse, New York City
Staatliches Museum für Völkerkunde, Munich
Nelson-Atkins Gallery of Art, Kansas City, Mo.
Norton Gallery and School of Art, West Palm Beach, Fla.
The University Museum, University of Pennsylvania, Philadelphia
The Art Museum, Princeton University
Royal Ontario Museum, Toronto
The Sackler Collections, New York City
City Art Museum of Saint Louis
Seattle Art Museum
Mr. Laurence Sickman, Kansas City, Mo.
Dr. Paul Singer, Summit, N.J.
Stanford University Art Museum
Victoria & Albert Museum, London
Worcester Art Museum
Yale University Art Gallery, New Haven

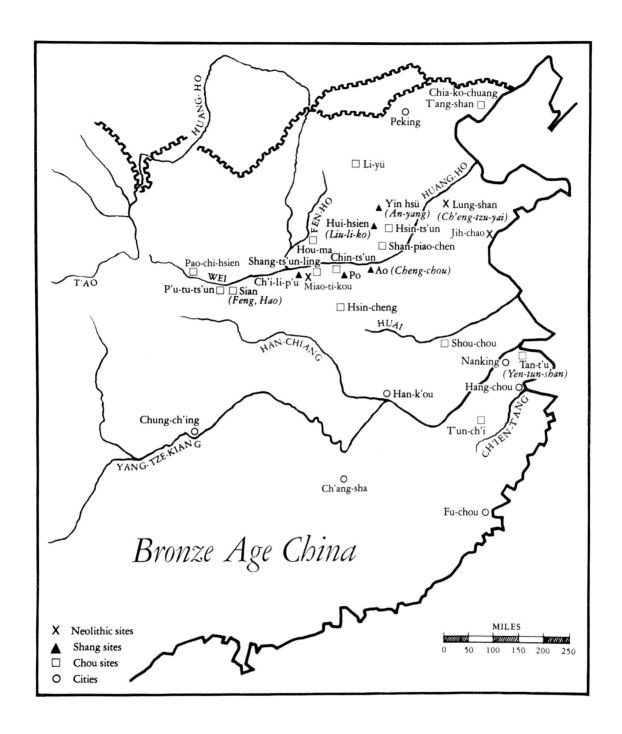

HUANG-HO

Chia-ko-chuang
T'ang-shan □

O
Peking

□ Li-yü

FEN-HO

▲ Yin hsü
(An-yang)

HUANG-HO

X Lung-shan
(Ch'eng-tzu-yai)

Hui-hsien ▲
(Liu-li-ko)

□ Hsin-ts'un

Jih-chao X

Hou-ma

□ Shan-piao-chen

Pao-chi-hsien   Shang-ts'un-ling   Chin-ts'un
□   WEI   □   ▲ Po   ▲ Ao (Cheng-chou)
                Ch'i-li-p'u ▲ X
P'u-tu-ts'un □ □ Sian   Miao-ti-kou
         (Feng, Hao)

T'AO

□ Hsin-cheng

HUAI

□ Shou-chou

Nanking O   □ Tan-t'u
              (Yen-tun-shan)

HAN-CHIANG

O Han-k'ou

Hang-chou O

Chung-ch'ing
O   □ T'un-ch'i
                                              CH'IEN-T'ANG

YANG-TZE-KIANG

O
Ch'ang-sha

Fu-chou O

Bronze Age China

X Neolithic sites
▲ Shang sites
□ Chou sites
O Cities

MILES

0   50   100   150   200   250

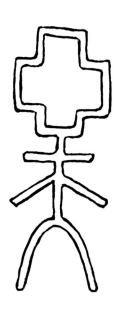

INTRODUCTION

To the forms of art that arose in the Bronze Age civilizations of the Old World, China made a contribution of unique character: the ritual bronze vessel of the Shang and Chou. In these celebrated vessels we are faced with the first manifestation of Chinese plastic thought. Their shapes and their décor are readily distinguished and unmistakable—unlike that of China's Neolithic pottery with its undeniable West-Asian flavor, the very pottery from which not a few of the bronze shapes ultimately descended.

These ancient vessels are important on three counts. In the first place, many of them bear inscriptions and thus represent a large body of authentic epigraphic records which, on the one hand, may confirm or supplement traditional history, and on the other hand supplies the palaeographic evidence for a complete history of the Chinese script. Secondly, these vessels are universally admired for their unsurpassed technical skill, the existence of primitive pieces and a fair number of crudely cast examples notwithstanding. But most important is the fact that they are works of art. Spanning virtually without interruption a time of nearly a millennium and a half, the bronzes are the true monuments on which to rely for the history of art in China's antiquity.

What is the level of this art, and what is its place among the arts? To a collector of the rank of an Alfred F. Pillsbury these vessels were, simply, "the greatest of all arts." To James M. Menzies, a scholar steeped in Chinese antiquarian studies, they represented "the quintessence of Chinese culture." Absolute evaluations, however, lie beyond our enquiry, which is an historical one. What we must keep in mind is that the bronze vessels, during Shang and Chou, were to all appearances the supreme art form, just as was pottery in Neolithic times. The shapes of the most primitive bronzes are pottery shapes. But the bronze casters, soon aware of the potentialities of their new medium, began to exploit them in shapes of increasing complexity. By the latter part of Shang they arrived at structures of architectonic rather than ceramic character.

Of course, not every bronze vessel was designed on architectonic principles. Some retained the simple forms of their ceramic ancestors; others were shaped as animal figures in the round. The latter clearly fall into the category of sculpture, since their function as containers neither requires nor determines their animal shape. The same, however, can be said of the architectonic quality present in so many late Shang bronzes: their function does not require or modify, let alone determine, that formal quality. Neither can that quality be regarded as an inevitable result of the physical properties of the material, the alloy of copper and tin called bronze. Now, if this architectonic quality is neither founded on functional considerations nor explainable on grounds of the properties of the material, what was the force that engendered it? It was a force, we must conclude, concerned with appearance or with form alone, an aesthetic urge, fulfilled through artistic consciousness.

If in the observable metamorphoses of the shapes there is indeed revealed the presence of artistic consciousness, the question of whether these vessels were the products of craftsmen or the creations of artists is all but answered. None of the bronzes, however, were the work of a single individual. Participating in their production were designers, modelers and mold-makers (of whom the latter two must have been master potters), together with smelters, furnace builders, bellows makers, and casters: the foundry gang, in a word, under the direction of a master craftsman. Changes of form and style, however, do not take place automatically, nor are they the result of group endeavor; they presuppose an intense concern for minutiae of design on the part of the responsible master, whether he be called craftsman or artist. Moreover, the apparent logic in the "evolution" of the shapes indicates that within tradition—the workshop tradition of techniques and models—there existed the master's freedom to make changes on purely formal grounds, counseled by artistic intelligence alone, without interference from the outside. The artist, "being the master mind, . . . would not expect or endure advice from any man as to how he should do his own work," wrote Herbert Maryon in a review touching upon an assumed "preoccupation of the vessel designer with technicalities" (*The Art Bulletin*, XLV/4, December, 1963, 394 f.).

The fact that the bronzes are anonymous works does not diminish their artistic importance. Speaking of painting, Etienne Gilson in his *Painting and Reality* (1957) said, "From the point of view of art taken precisely qua art, there is nothing to lose in considering all paintings anonymous."

Our exhibition is concerned with the artistic aspect of the bronzes. It attempts to make their stylistic sequence intelligible, especially that of the early phases, Shang and Western Chou. Of the eighty pieces exhibited, no less than forty are assigned to the Shang period; twenty, to Western Chou; the remaining twenty, to Eastern Chou and Han. Accordingly the viewer is able to examine the early material in great detail and to form a reasonably complete picture of the development of both the vessel shapes and ornamental designs. The late Western Chou and Eastern Chou material, by contrast, represents the consecutive styles in more sweeping perspective. With but a few exceptions the exhibition consists entirely of vessels, so that the same types may be seen in several versions, typifying consecutive stylistic stages. It goes without saying that all of the bronzes which might ideally be included in an exhibition of this kind are not available for display. But it is gratifying to note that as many as twenty pieces, one fourth of the total, have never been shown or published before.

Seen in the entire perspective of Chinese art history, most of the decorative designs on Shang and Chou bronzes may be characterized as purely ornamental. They were typical creations of a phase that preceded representational art, the art concerned with, and dependent on, reality. The shift toward representation occurred during the Han period. The moment it occurred, the art of the ornament—heretofore the art of greatest consequence—took second place and began to stagnate. It is a noteworthy fact that at the same time the day of the bronze vessel, too, was over.

References to reality are not altogether wanting in the decoration of the vessels. As early as Shang there appear among the invented zoomorphs either parts or, more rarely, whole figures of recognizable animals such as the water buffalo, the tiger, the stag, the elephant, and the owl; but they do not affect the ornamental quality of the décor as a whole. Moreover, while unambiguous as images, these animal figures are constructed largely of the same elements as the zoomorphs and harmonize with them. No action is ever portrayed; the relationship of these static images one with another is merely that of formal arrangement. When, in the Warring States period or in late Ch'un-ch'iu times, hunting scenes and representations of banquets, archery contests, and musicians and dancers came into favor, these engraved pictures, the first signs of a nascent pictorial art, did not actually compete with ornamental art. As pictures, they remained semi-diagrammatic, while from the decorative point of view they are ineffectual. But most important is the fact that, measured by the sophistication and elegance of coeval ornamental art, the engravings are groping, artless, and as yet inexpressive pictographic records rather than art.

From the beginning geometric motifs occur side by side with zoomorphic motifs. The latter are a Shang innovation, and the story of Shang ornamental design is the story of their unfolding and "growth" from rudimentary and vaguely suggested, semi-geometric forms to neatly defined, fully zoomorphic forms. The typical décor of the Neolithic pottery was limited to geometric patterns: the spiral, the lozenge, serration or zigzags, meanders, and interlocked T's. With the exception of the spiral and spiral-derived dynamic patterns of almost floral character—as in the painted wares from Hsi-yin-ts'un, Southwest Shansi, and Miao-ti-kou, West Honan—which had already disappeared from the late Neolithic repertoire, all of these geometric patterns occur in bronzes, gray pottery, and white pottery of the Shang period. But in contrast to the new, zoomorphic designs they remained the same throughout Shang, save that their execution changed from flat relief to high relief in accordance with stylistic changes in general.

To prevent any possible misunderstanding that might arise from the word "spiral," I hasten to add that small spirals in dense patterns, distinct from the large, sweeping S-curves of the Neolithic spirals, play an essential part in Shang ornamentation. In fact, their varying configurations were the matrix from which the zoomorphic images sprang. Consisting of nothing but spirals and eyes or pairs of eyes, these zoomorphs were by no means abstractions, but sheer design. The phenomenon we are faced with here has been clearly described in a passage in Susanne K. Langer's *Feeling and Form* (1953), Chapter Five:

"The fundamental forms which occur in the decorative arts of all ages and races—for instance the circle, the triangle, the spiral, the parallel—are known as *motifs* of design. They are not art 'works,' not even ornaments, themselves, but they lend themselves to composition, and are therefore incentives to artistic creation. . . . A comparative study of decorative art and primitive representational art suggests forcibly that *form is first*, and the representational function accrues to it."

Gradually, with existing designs offering the thematic material for new versions, some of which fell by the wayside, there emerged a series of standardized, successful zoomorphic images, the familiar "dragons" of late Shang.

The stylistic phases of this development will become quite clear, I believe, through the descriptions given in this catalogue. In accordance with a conception formulated by me in an article, "The Bronze Styles of the Anyang Period" (*ACASA*, VII, 1953), the phases are designated as Shang I–V. Excavations carried out in China during the intervening years have shown that this sequence is fundamentally correct. A brief summary of the five styles of Shang zoomorphic decoration may be added here for convenient orientation:

Style I: Thin relief lines; simple forms; light, airy effect.
Style II: Relief ribbons; harsh, heavy forms; incised appearance.
Style III: Dense, fluent, more curvilinear figurations developed from the preceding style.
Style IV: First separation of motifs proper from spirals, which now become small and function as ground pattern. Motifs and spirals are flush.
Style V: First appearance of motifs in relief: the motifs rise above the ground spirals, which may be eliminated altogether.

It would take us too far to broaden this brief outline by a similar presentation of the typological changes of the vessels' shapes, which corroborate and help to establish the sequence of the styles of decoration. It should be mentioned, however, that the thorough investigations of casting techniques and mold forms from An-yang undertaken by Li Chi and Wan Chia-pao have led to a sequential classification that appears to correspond, more or less, with the technical side of the décor styles outlined above. Their classification comprises four categories:

A—Simple, incised mold design.
B—Composite model-mold design.
C—Engraving and appliqué on model.
D—Relief on model.

The first of these categories agrees with Style I; the second, with the frequent combination on one vessel of Styles I and II; the third answers to the techniques of Styles II, III, IV; and the fourth squarely corresponds to Style V.

The sequence of the five styles offers a chance of seeing continuity in Shang decorative design. The system makes sense, historically, because it permits us to determine the relative date of a decorated vessel. Absolute dates, however desirable, are of secondary importance unless the relative position of an individual vessel is fully understood. For the Shang period there is virtually no possibility of relying on inscribed bronzes to establish a chronological sequence anyway; most of the vessels are uninscribed.

If the ornaments on Shang bronzes came into being as sheer design, form based on form alone, configurations without reference to reality or, at best, with dubious allusions to reality, then, we are almost forced to conclude, they cannot have had any ascertainable meaning—religious, cosmological, or mythological—meaning, at any rate, of an established, literary kind. Quite possibly these ornaments were iconographically meaningless, or meaningful only as pure form—like musical forms and therefore unlike literary definitions. Perhaps we may expect some guidance in an attempt to answer this question by relying quite simply on the form of the ornaments themselves: do they not stand somewhere between the geometric and organic realms, unidentifiable with either? Perhaps, therefore, we must renounce attempts to explain these elusive images in terms of cosmology or religious lore, not to mention the naive idea that the zoomorphs reflect the Shang nobility's passion for hunting. Not by choice but of necessity do all writings on the subject of symbolism in bronze decoration depend on identifiable images of real beasts. But the identifiable images are greatly outnumbered by the zoomorphs which are design merely, interesting solely on formal grounds, as "pure art."

When precisely did the Chinese begin to experiment with metalworking and the casting of bronzes? Tradition ascribes bronze to the Hsia. But so far the archaeological record does not support the tradition. The Hsia Dynasty, if it existed, must have been largely coeval with the late Neolithic Black Pottery culture called Honan Lung-shan. The following stage, known as Lo-ta-miao—from a site at Cheng-chou, Honan, discovered in 1956, which seems to bracket the end of Hsia or predynastic Shang and early Shang—is still a pre-metal stage. A site representing the same horizon, Erh-li-t'ou, east of Lo-yang, only excavated from 1959 to 1964 and considered as the first Shang capital (Western Po), yielded nothing but a few primitive bronze things such as arrowheads, awls, fishhooks, a shapeless knife, and one small bell. These were all locally made, no doubt, since there were also found "a number of unworked lumps of metal and pieces of slag, as well as vaguely denominated 'clay moulds,'" according to Alexander C. Soper's account in "Early, Middle, and Late Shang" (*AA*, XXVIII, 1966). The primitive nature of this assemblage is emphasized by the total absence of bronze vessels. The evidence for early Shang metallurgy provided by this modest aggregation seems to indicate that vessels of bronze came into being only toward, or in, Middle Shang. Numerous sites and burials around Cheng-chou, about 50 miles east of Erh-li-t'ou and believed to be identical with the Middle Shang capital of Ao, reveal a much more advanced stage of the bronze industry. The types of bronze vessels found at Cheng-chou, some of them primitive, all of them early in style, range, apparently, from Shang I to Shang III. These early styles, therefore, appear to have been current before the move under P'an Keng to the place called Yin, in Northern Honan, that was to be the last capital of the Shang (archaeologically known as Yin-hsü or An-yang). Styles IV and V appear only afterwards.

Venturing to translate into absolute dates what the incomplete archaeological record, history, and an unsettled chronology suggest, we may conclude that Styles I–III were developed after the move from Po to Ao, when Ao was the capital—1562–1389 B.C. in the reckoning of Liu Hsin's *San-t'ung-li*, or about 1400–1300 B.C. according to the shorter chronology of the *Bamboo Annals*. By the same token, Styles IV and V would date from the time when Yin was the capital, 1388–1122 B.C. or about 1300–1028 B.C., respectively, although it is important to note that the Ao styles (I, II, III) were still living styles in the early An-yang or Yin-hsü phase typified by the finds from Hsiao-t'un.

The picture of the early stage of vessel casting offered by the Cheng-chou finds is supplemented, as well as confirmed, by the harvest of pre-An-yang material excavated at Liu-li-ko in Hui-hsien, Northern Honan. In addition, of course, there is an abundance of relevant but archaeologically unattested material in various collections which greatly enriches our knowledge of early Shang art.

When the Chou destroyed Shang, in 1122 (according to Liu Hsin, who died in A.D. 23), or 1111 (according to I-hsing [673–727] and Tung Tso-pin), or 1070 (Yin-li School of the Later Han), or 1066 (Wang Kuo-wei), or about 1050 (*Bamboo Annals*; W. Perceval Yetts), or in 1047 (*Shih-chi*), or 1038 (James M. Menzies), or 1027 (Ch'en Meng-chia; B. Karlgren; H. H. Dubs), or 1018 (Chou Fa-kao)—1027 being the now widely accepted date, they cannot have been ignorant of the superior level of Shang material culture. Rather they may have been anxious to attract to themselves the services of the metropolitan artisans, for no rupture to speak of seems to have occurred in the production of sacrificial vessels of high quality for the ancestral shrines of the Chou nobility. And while there are signs of a taste not quite compatible with Shang tradition in some early Western Chou and possibly predynastic Chou bronzes (see Nos. 41, 50), others offer no hint of change at all (e.g. No. 48).

A survey of Western Chou bronzes datable by their inscriptions gives the impression of a measure of provincial distinctness in the earliest Chou years, followed by a complete acceptance of the late Shang style in the reigns of K'ang Wang and Chao Wang in circles close to the royal court. By that time, however, new tendencies found expression in sweeping, curvilinear designs, especially of large birds (see Nos. 49, 51, 52), which make the designs in the Shang fashion seem somewhat antiquated. From the reign of Mu Wang onward, still within the first hundred years of Chou rule, the Western

Chou style moved rapidly, for better or worse, away from lingering Shang reminiscences. The old zoomorphic images were transformed (see Nos. 57–60) and dissolved into rather jejune ribbons. The late Western Chou bronzes so decorated may assume a ponderous, uninspired air, and occasionally reveal a lack of precision that would have been inconceivable in any vessel of importance from the beginning of the dynasty. By the end of Western Chou the inexpressive, flattish bands were converted into a new variety of perfectly uniform dragon band, while the decorative system underwent a significant change as well. The old order of antithetically placed images was given up in favor of continuous patterns, covering the vessel's surface without regard to axial divisions. The new dragon bands, too, are treated as patterned elements (see No. 61). Without individuality, and ignominiously subordinated to a patterned order—inverted, twisted, or interlocked—they have lost the character of true images.

If Western Chou, in a broad view, may be seen as a phase during which the powerful Shang tradition was slowly eliminated, Eastern Chou by contrast (beginning in 770 B.C. when the Chou court was forced to give up its Western capitals of Feng and Hao in Shensi and had to move eastward to Lo-yang in Honan) was a period of 550 years of ceaseless artistic inventiveness and utmost brilliance.

The history of these 550 years of ornamental art has yet to be written. But a beginning was made when L. Bachhofer, in his *Short History of Chinese Art* (1946), was able to replace the historically inarticulate categories such as "Third Phase" or "Huai Style," then in use, by a logically comprehensible stylistic sequence covering the time span of Eastern Chou. His sequence comprised the following styles: Hsin-cheng—Li-yü—Huai—Chin-ts'un. The new and considerable information that has reached us from China since then was taken into account in W. Watson's *Ancient Chinese Bronzes* (1962), where the same sequence is retained except that it opens with Shang-ts'un-ling, an early Eastern Chou assemblage from the San-men Gorge area in Western Honan antedating 655 B.C.; it is further elaborated by the introduction of new material from Shansi (Hou-ma and Fen-shui-ling), Hopei (Chia-ko-chuang in T'ang-shan-hsien), Anhui (Shou-hsien: tomb of the Marquis Chao of Ts'ai, who reigned 518–491 B.C.), and the south. Close analyses of the Hsin-cheng and Li-yü styles in particular are given in C. D. Weber's recent investigation of pictorial bronze vessels in *AA*, XXVIII/2–3 and 4 (1966) and XXIX/2–3 (1967). The date of the Chin-ts'un graves near Lo-yang, Honan, was established by B. Karlgren, "Notes on a Kin-ts'un Album" (*BMFEA*, X, 1938), as approximately 450–230 B.C.

A perfectly distinct style, represented by a *ting* tripod from the Royal Ontario Museum (No. 63), whose décor of interlocked, angular meander bands with a plain border at one side is encountered among the material excavated at Hou-ma, Shansi, and Liu-li-ko, Northern Honan, has not been recognized so far within the Eastern Chou sequence. This style falls between the Hsin-cheng and Li-yü styles but cannot be identified with either. It might provisionally be called "proto-Li-yü" or "style of the interlocked meander bands." The structure of the classical Li-yü pattern, very unlike that of the Hsin-cheng pattern, seems to be adumbrated in this "proto-Li-yü" style. If this style is taken into account, the sequence of Eastern Chou styles—disregarding phases within styles, as well as languishing survivals—may be drawn up as follows:

Shang-ts'un-ling VIII–VII c. (example of the period: No. 61)
Hsin-cheng   VII–VI c. (late example: No. 62)
Proto-Li-yü   VII–VI c. (typical example: No. 63)
Li-yü   VI–V c. (advanced example: No. 64)
Huai   V–IV c. (typical example: No. 65)
Chin-ts'un   V–III c. (diverse examples: Nos. 69–78)

Through the Huai style, the décor was executed in cast relief, as in the past. In the Chin-ts'un style, however, relief was replaced by colorful inlays of metal or semiprecious stones: copper, silver, and gold, turquoise and malachite. These inlays are arranged in geometric patterns of such simplicity as to suggest an extreme reaction against the graceful froth of the Huai style. But it did not take long for the designers of inlay to arrive at exceedingly complicated patterns of geometric character (e.g.

No. 70) or of a half-geometric, half-zoomorphic nature (e.g. No. 76), both of which are grand inventions within the sphere of pure form without any reference to external reality. They were also the last such inventions.

For when, in Han times, there arose an art form concerning itself with the visual aspects of reality and endeavoring to establish them in expressive images, the days of a purely ornamental art were over. The surfaces of a vessel were no longer an adequate medium for the new, pictorial art whose genesis marks the end of antiquity and of the long uncontested art of the vessel.

CHRONOLOGICAL TABLE

	Trad. Dates	Tung Tso-pin	*Bamboo Annals*	Ch'en, Karlgren
HSIA DYNASTY	2205	2183	1989	—
SHANG DYNASTY				
Capital Po	1766	1751	1558	1523
Capital Ao	1562	1568	1400	—
Capital Yin	1388	1384	1301	1300
CHOU DYNASTY				
Wu Wang	1122	1111	1050	1027
Ch'eng Wang	1115	1104	1044	1024
K'ang Wang	1078	1067	1007	1004
Chao Wang	1052	1041	981	984
Mu Wang	1001	1023	962	965
Kung Wang	946	982	907	927
I Wang	934	966	895	907
Hsiao Wang	909	954	870	897
Yi Wang	894	924	861	887
Li Wang	878	878	853	857
Kung-ho Regency	841	841	841	841

Hsüan Wang	827
Yu Wang	781
EASTERN CHOU	
Capital Lo-yang (Ch'eng Chou)	770
Spring and Autumn Period	722
Warring States Period	481
End of the Chou Dynasty	256
CH'IN DYNASTY	221
WESTERN HAN DYNASTY	206 B.C.
Wang Mang Interregnum	A.D. 9–24
EASTERN HAN DYNASTY	A.D. 25–220

1　PEI, TUMBLER
Perhaps Early Shang
H. 6½ in., W. 4 in.
Ashmolean Museum, Oxford

The slightly convex sides of this cylindrical vessel taper toward a narrow, flat, circular base. Its shape is of utter simplicity, but of pleasing proportions and not unrefined. The metal is very thin, corroded, and brittle. The shape is not encountered among the known types of Shang and Chou bronzes, and there is no decoration to give any hint as to the stylistic position of this extraordinary piece. This tumbler seems more archaic and remote than any of the Shang bronzes now known.

　　Not previously published.

So little does this piece fit into our picture of Chinese bronzes that we might feel inclined to ask whether it is at all Chinese. If its Chinese origin is certain, its date would have to be very early because it is quite unlikely that a completely atypical shape such as this tumbler's would appear among the known, more or less standardized types. Its early date, however, does not depend exclusively on logic. The shape has analogues among the pottery beakers, *Pei*, of the late Neolithic Lung-shan period as well as of early Shang. The Lung-shan specimens may be purely cylindrical in shape like those from Ch'ing-ku-tui, Liang-shan, Shantung (*Kaogu*, 1962/1, p. 29, fig. 4:1, 2), or flare at the mouth, as does a piece from Ch'eng-tzu-yai, Shantung (*Ch'eng-tzu-yai*, pl. 17:1,

pl. 30:1); they do not greatly differ from late Yang-shao pottery types (e.g., *Miao-ti-kou Monograph*, pl. 41:7). The early Shang site of Erh-li-t'ou in Honan has yielded a comparable beaker type of less slender proportions (*Kaogu*, 1965/5, pl. 4:12; Soper, "Early, Middle, and Late Shang," fig. 6:12), and among the finds from the Erh-li-kang site of Cheng-chou, Honan, is a tall cup with handle which, save for the handle, resembles the Oxford tumbler very closely (*Cheng-chou Erh-li-kang*, pls. 10:2 and 21:7).

　　Why this shape should not have entered into the series of classical Shang types is a question we cannot hope to answer. Possibly its early demise was due to the rise of the *Ku* beaker, ubiquitous in Shang archaeological assemblages.

2   KU
Shang, Style I
H. 7⁷⁄₁₆ in., DIAM. (at mouth) 5¹⁄₁₆ in.
Royal Ontario Museum, Toronto

A beaker with slender waist and flaring mouth rises from a hollow, splayed foot. The upper part of the foot, just below the bottom of the beaker, is pierced by three large, cross-shaped orifices. The vessel is decorated with geometric motifs in two friezes, neither of which is divided into sections or panels. Around the foot runs a band showing a relief design of flattish oval "eyes" connected by diagonal lines which tangentially join the oval rings around the eyes. The triangles above and below the diagonal tangents are filled with spirals or, rather, curls whose sizes accord with the given spaces. Around the waist runs a true meander band, lined by rows of circlets and "bowstrings."

Published: M. Loehr, "Bronze Styles," *ACASA*, VII, 1953, fig. 2.

In this early *Ku* type, the middle zone forms no bulge, and the cross-shaped holes in the foot are excessively large. Of the ornaments, the meander is particularly remarkable. It is distinct from the angular spirals known as *lei-wen*, or thunder pattern, in later bronzes; rather we may feel reminded of the meanders in some of the late Neolithic painted wares. Searching for the origin of the "eyed band with diagonals," in Karlgren's terminology, Li Chi, too, recognized potential prototypes among ornaments of both Painted and Black potteries; see his "Diverse Backgrounds," fig. 3. Among the *Ku* beakers excavated at Anyang, there is one single specimen to compare, a fragment whose waist zone, fortunately preserved, is decorated with a meander-like pattern of slightly later style (Li Chi and Wan Chia-pao, *Studies of the Bronze Ku-Beaker*, pl. 10 and p. 71, fig. 3: R 2015, from Hsiao-t'un; also Li Chi, "Studies of the Decorative Art of the Yin-Shang Period: Pt. I," pl. 6:1). The absence of a *Ku* with equally primitive décor among the material excavated at Anyang suggests an accordingly early date. One specimen in a collection in Peking, however, the décor of which is certainly no less primitive, reportedly came from Anyang in 1942 (*Yen-k'u chi-chin*, shang, 54; Loehr, "Bronze Styles," fig. 1). The large cross-shaped holes in the wall of the foot, by the way, support the early date required by the decoration, for in later versions of the *Ku* these holes are shaped like slender crosses of regular form or are dispensed with altogether. It is likely that these holes, which are seen also in other hollow-footed types, were a technical necessity, at least in the earlier phase: they indicate, it is assumed, passages through core and mold for dowels, pins, or chaplets used to suspend the foot-core above the bottom of the beaker core (cf. N. Barnard, *Bronze Casting and Bronze Alloys*, pp. 115–116; Li Chi and Wan Chia-pao, *op. cit.*, pp. 22–25). If this interpretation is correct, the presence of similar cross-shaped orifices in footed pottery vessels (e.g., *Cheng-chou Erh-li-kang*, pl. 7:4, drawings, pl. 6:5) would always presuppose a dependence on metal forms.

3   TSUN
Shang, Style I
H. 10¾ in., DIAM. 8¼ in.
The Sackler Collections, New York City

This deep, footed vessel with ovoid body has a sharply broken shoulder, wide cylindrical neck and everted lip. The foot is pierced by four cross-shaped openings, paired diametrically. The decoration is cast in relief executed in the simplest technique, that is, by incisions in the mold. Below the shoulder, at the widest part, the body is surrounded by a wide band lined with circlets above and below, and filled with three symmetrically designed T'ao-t'ieh faces. These faces consist of round and protuberant paired eyes, with curls, spirals, and attenuated hooks arranged about them. On the shoulder is a narrower band filled with similar, but simplified, faces with oval eyes. Two of these smaller units correspond to the 120-degree arc occupied by each large unit of the main zone. The upper parts of both neck and foot-ring are adorned with the simplest of all patterns, the relief lines called "bowstrings," disposed in groups of three. The surface is covered by a variegated, greenish patina.

Published: J. Young, *Art Styles of Ancient Shang*, No. 4.

To the writer's knowledge, this rare, archaic vessel is the oldest of its type on record. A single example of this type was found in the upper level of Erh-li-kang, Cheng-chou (*KKHP*, XV, 1957/1, p. 53 ff., pl. 3 : 1); its décor is arranged in the same order, but it is stylistically more advanced. Several specimens have been excavated in Hsiao-t'un, Anyang; stockier in proportions and more lavishly decorated, none of them is earlier than Style III (Li Chi, *The Beginnings*, pls. 34, 35; S. Umehara, *Inkyo*, pls. 64:3, 66:1). In two of these vessels, the décor zones have increased to four, so that only the neck and a narrow strip at the lower part of the body remain bare. And, on the shoulder of Umehara's second example (previously published in *KKHP*, III, 1948, Li Chi, "Studies of Hsiao-t'un Bronzes," Pt. I, pl. 3:3) there appear in low relief three bovine heads such as in a later phase assume the plastic vigor seen in the large *Tsun* of the Metropolitan Museum, No. 29, and from Cologne, No. 30.

Apparently this type disappeared from the classical repertory of late Shang vessels. This circumstance may be the reason why the type is so rare, and why even its name is lost. The designations used today vary widely: *Lei* (*KKHP*, XV), *P'ou* (Li Chi), *Hu* (Umehara). But all of these names are universally adopted as the traditional names of standard bronze types (e.g., our Nos. 15, 17, 42). It would be confusing to transfer any of these names to a wholly distinct type of vessel. The term "Tsun" seems justifiable insofar as this type agrees with the trumpet-mouthed *Tsun* (e.g., No. 29) so well in all essential aspects—except for the wide mouth—that they seem like variations of the same basic type; and, it is conceivable that the early disappearance of the type here described, No. 3, was caused by a preference for the statelier, wide-mouthed shape. The latter shape is found with Style III décor in a specimen in Shanghai (Mizuno, *Bronzes and Jades*, pl. 19 C; also Chêng Tê-k'un, *Shang China*, pl. 51 A), and with early Style IV(?) décor in a piece excavated at Hsiao-t'un (Li Chi, *The Beginnings*, pl. 33). It seems, therefore, that the present type began earlier than the trumpet-mouthed type, and that its days were numbered when Style III began to wane.

4 CHIA
Shang, Style I
H. 13 in., DIAM. 7½ in.
Avery Brundage Collection, M. H. de Young Memorial Museum, San Francisco

A round vessel with flat bottom stands on three slanting, triangular, pointed legs. Above the lowest part, the vessel contracts, then flares toward the rim that is wider in diameter than the rest. On the rim, which is strengthened by a ledge of smithied appearance, stand two upright posts capped by mushroom-like tops with whorl designs around a knob in the center of each. The posts, quadrangular in section, do not stand in opposition or diametrically, but are set relatively close to each other. Opposite the segment marked by these posts, a broad handle with a median "seam" arches from the hip of the vessel toward a point below the rim. The bulging hip is decorated with a frieze composed of three sections, showing fine patterns of thread relief in symmetrical arrangement around pairs of round, bulbous eyes. A second frieze in thread relief, but without eyes, girdles the narrower waist. Both friezes are lined with rows of circlets.

Published: R. Y. Lefebvre d'Argencé, *Ancient Chinese Bronzes in the Avery Brundage Collection*, pl. I A.

From the technical point of view, the décor corresponds to the style category *Shang I*. But the design of the ornaments reveals considerable refinement, and the contour of the eyes, in particular, suggests a more advanced stage than typified by such examples as the Berlin *Ho* (O. Kümmel, *Chinesische Bronzen*, pls. 5–7; Loehr, "Bronze Styles," fig. 4) or the *Ting* from Liu-li-ko (*Hui-hsien Report*, pl. 14:1; *Archaeology in New China*, pl. 29:3).

5   CHÜEH
Shang, Style II
H. 6½ in., w. 6½ in.
Yale University Art Gallery, New Haven; Hobart and Edward Small Moore Memorial
Collection, gift of Mrs. William H. Moore

This tripod, with its pointed-oval cross-section, has thin, triangular legs placed in a perpendicular position. The body is acutely articulated. Its flat-bottomed lower part is joined by a receding curve to the strongly contracted, straight waist. The upper part projects far outward on both sides, forming a very long spout to the left of the handle and a pointed tip or "tail" to the right of the handle. Where the narrow, V-shaped spout emerges from the sides of the cup there rise two small, somewhat shapeless posts, topped by short bars. These posts are an unusual and patently primitive feature. There are other primitive features: the rim is folded over, rather than strengthened by a cast ledge; the handle, too, appears to have been folded, so that it must have been fashioned from a separate sheet of metal cast onto, or fused with, the body; finally, the decoration of the waist zone is done in a technique fundamentally different from that used in casting, that is, by embossing or chasing. The relieved parts of the décor, in other words, appear as intaglio on the inner side. The ornament consists of two T'ao-t'ieh faces centered on the sides; they closely resemble those of a Style II *Chia* from the Sackler Collections, No. 8, save that their eyes are more angular and are flush with the surrounding parts.

Not previously published, but mentioned in S. H. Hansford, "Pre-Anyang," *OA*, IV/1, Spring 1958, pp. 3, 4.

If the description of the rim as being doubled is correct, we might venture a step further and ask whether the enigmatic feature of the small posts at the spout was not, perhaps, related to the process of doubling the rim? It is obvious that an excess of metal would result from the sheet's being folded down, an excess that would either have to be removed or somehow to be given shape. The posts or arches might represent attempts to solve the problem in two possible ways. There can be no certainty, however, unless we find some example that would exhibit the surmised cause, i.e., the excess, in an unambiguous manner.

What must be taken into account, in addition, is the formation of the spout in pottery *Chüeh*. "In the early ceramic forms, there appears, not infrequently, at the junction of the spout and rim, a pair of loops added to strengthen these joints. These mud loops were most probably the budding uprights which attained their mature development only in the bronze form, . . ." (Li Chi, *Studies of the Bronze Chüeh-Cup*, p. 130). But the relationships between pottery *Chüeh* and bronze *Chüeh* are not sufficiently well known to warrant definite statements. Technically, the clay *Chüeh* spout does not require a strengthening; nor would the loops really so function. It is conceivable that despite the generally observable dependence of the bronze vessel shapes on pottery shapes a

detail such as the upright posts of the *Chüeh*, as well as of the *Chia*, was first established in metal forms and then perfunctorily imitated or merely suggested in clay.

The most interesting question posed by the Yale specimen, which obligingly was brought to the writer's attention by the curator, George Lee, concerns its dissimilarity from ceramic types. Yet it is equally distinct from the common round-bodied bronze forms of this class. It seems that this specimen represents a third tradition—neither derived from the late Neolithic pottery tradition, nor to be equated with the tradition of bronze casting as typified by the overwhelmingly large number of ordinary cast bronzes of Shang date. This third tradition becomes apparent in all of the features pointing toward smithying rather than casting.

Though rare, this specimen does not stand alone as far as its shape is concerned. A piece with similar décor and two rudimentary posts is in the Royal Ontario Museum (B. Stephen, "Early Chinese Bronzes," p. 62, fig. 1); a plain piece is owned by Dr. Paul Singer (Loehr, *Relics*, p. 36, fig. 6); another one was excavated in Hui-hsien (*Hui-hsien Report*, pl. 13) and two came from a Cheng-chou site named Ming-kung-lu West (*Kaogu*, 1965/10, p. 501, figs. 15, 16). All these examples show similarly thin, triangular, and more or less vertically placed legs.

6   CHÜEH
     Shang, Style I–II
     H. 9⅛ in., W. 6¾ in.
     Seattle Art Museum; gift of Mr. and Mrs. Herbert Brink

Three slanting, rather slight, triangular, pointed legs support this oval vessel with flat bottom. As in the early *Chia* types the body is built up in zones resembling hips and waist, while its upper part sweeps into an assymetrical, wing-like shape, forming a long, open spout at one side, and a balancing pointed projection at the other side. Where the rim dips, in the middle, a flat handle issuing from the hip joins the upper portion of the wall. A curious, pointed arch surmounted by a steep cone straddles the sides of the spout near its base. There are two friezes: the upper one, lined on top with a row of circlets, shows widely spaced curvilinear motifs in thread relief lines; the lower one, by contrast, exhibits the dense relief pattern of Style II, having a mask with bulging oval eyes in the center and curvilinear extensions to both sides—comparable to the decoration of the *Chia* from The Sackler Collections, No. 8. This piece is said to have been found at Liu-li-ko, Hui-hsien, Honan.

   Published: *ACASA*, XVII, 1963, p. 54; Seattle Art Museum *Engagement Book*, 1964, opp. April 19; Millard B. Rogers, "Recent Acquisitions of the Seattle Art Museum," *Archaeology*, Winter 1964, p. 264.

The combination of the two distinct relief styles is fairly common among archaic vessels. It may be seen in a *Chüeh* from the "Prince Kung of Sung Set" in the Royal Ontario Museum (White, *Bronze Culture*, pl. 78 B; Stephen, "Early Chinese Bronzes," fig. 3), a type with two posts instead of the pointed arch of the Seattle piece, or in a *Chia* of the Shanghai Museum (Mizuno, *Bronzes and Jades*, pl. 18 D; Chêng Tê-k'un, *Shang China*, pl. 48 A).

7   LI-HO
Shang, Style II
H. 9⅝ in., w. (including handle) 7 in.
Avery Brundage Collection, M. H. de Young Memorial Museum, San Francisco

This spouted vessel is shaped like a *Li* tripod with slanting, hollow, pointed legs. The cylindrical upper part of the body is topped by a dome, with a large opening reminiscent of a wide-open mouth. Apparently the resemblance to a mouth induced the designer to add a nose and two eyes on the dome, thus transforming it into a vaguely human face. Below the mouth is a handle, attached to a horizontal plate that links it to the rim, which is joined to one leg, not far from the tip. Opposite the handle a tall tubular spout rises from the dome. The neck is circled by a narrow zone of zoomorphic ornament in low relief, apparently done by carving the model: centered on the grooves between the legs are three masks, with slightly protruding oval eyes, surrounded by curls and laterally framed by hands and hooks. The forms lack regularity and refinement. A light green patina with patches of dark green covers the bronze.

Published: d'Argencé, *Brundage Bronzes*, pl. I B.

Surprisingly, this archaic type is matched by another, apparently still earlier, version in the same collection, a vessel of almost identical structure but decorated with a strikingly primitive, blurred and thin T'ao-t'ieh band of Style I (fig. I). The décor of this vessel that was exhibited at Asia House Gallery in January, 1968 (Lefebvre d'Argencé, *Chinese Treasures from the Avery Brundage Collection*, No. 1), is remarkable for two very unusual features: the eyes are indicated by outlines only, rather than by protrusions, and the upper and lower borders are marked with small raised dots instead of the common circlets. The spout slightly widens toward the top. Both this shape of the spout and an unadulterated Style I raised-line T'ao-t'ieh frieze are shared by the long-known *Li-Ho* of the Berlin Museum (Kümmel, *Chinesische Bronzen*, pls. 5–7; J. L. Davidson, "Toward a Grouping of Early Chinese Bronzes," *Parnassus*, IX, 1937, p. 51; Loehr, "Bronze Styles," fig. 4; Jung Keng, *Shang Chou*, II, fig. 486; Umehara, *Seika*, II, pl. 142, with rubbing of a detail of the ornament). A third specimen to compare resembles our No. 7 most closely, except for the spout which tapers like those of the Berlin and Brundage specimens just mentioned; it is a vessel decorated in Style II that was found near the Huan River in the Anyang area (Sun Hai-po, *Honan chi-chin t'u-chih sheng-kao*, No. 23; Jung Keng, *op. cit.*, II, fig. 487).

Vessels of spouted type in late Neolithic pottery are the likely antecedents of this rare bronze type. They first appear in the tripod-ewer shape, with tall open spout and handle, of the Lung-shan phase, as at Ch'eng-tzu-yai, Shantung (*Ch'eng-tzu-yai Report*, color frontispiece and pls. 28, 29), at Jih-chao in Liang-ch'eng, Shantung (fig. A; Th. Dexel, *Die*

Formen chinesischer Keramik, 1955, pl. 5 C; Chêng Tê-k'un, *Prehistoric China*, 1959, pl. 30), or at An-ch'iu, Shantung (fig. B; *Archaeology in New China*, pl. 15:4). This tripod-ewer, which is known as *Kuei* or *K'uei*, a character written with the radical *Li* "tripod with hollow legs," occurs in a variant with rudimentary spout among the related wares from the important K'o-hsing-chuang site in Shensi (fig. C; *Feng-hsi Monograph*, p. 61, pl. 29:2). Still farther west, in Kansu Province, pottery spouted vessels with domed top and tubular spout on baluster-shaped bodies with handles evoking metal prototypes, closely resembling the bronzes under discussion, belong with the typical inventory of the Ch'i-chia culture (fig. D; J. G. Andersson, "Researches into the Prehistory of the Chinese," *BMFEA*, XV, 1943, pls. 37:4 and 38; cf. Chêng Tê-k'un, *Prehistoric China*, pl. 40:2,3). A crudely potted *Li-Ho* with a fully developed spout of tubular form which looks like a derivative of the K'o-hsing-chuang type mentioned (fig. C), was found as far south as Shih-chia-ho in Hupei (Chêng Tê-k'un, *ibidem*, pl. 42:1).

The basic structure of the four archaic bronze *Ho* or *Li-Ho* is still recognizable in the monumental tetrapod-ewers of the Nezu Museum in Tokyo, which date from the late Shang period (Umehara, *Seizansō seishō*, VI, pls. 1–8; Mizuno, *Bronzes and Jades*, pls. 42, 43 and color pl. 7), and the powerful mask with open mouth on the square dome of each of the Nezu *Ho* is prefigured in the timidly suggested face on the dome of the Brundage piece.

A different type of early, spouted ewer, with a globular body on solid feet like those of archaic *Ting* vessels, is the *Ho* from Munich, No. 11.

A. Shantung

B. Shantung

C. Shensi

D. Kansu

Fig. 1

8   CHIA
Shang, Style II
H. 8¼ in., DIAM. 5¾ in.
The Sackler Collections, New York City

The round vessel with flat bottom is supported by three slanting, pointed legs whose cross-section approaches the shape of an irregular rhombus. A simple, broad handle swings in a wide arc from the lower, bulging part of the vessel to the upper, flaring part, and is joined to the rim by a short, wedge-shaped, upright flange on top of the handle. From the strengthened rim rises a pair of quadrangular posts with convex, mushroom-like tops with sunken whorl designs. The segment between these posts measures less than one third of the perimeter. Except for a sharply cast band in three sections, the surface is plain and smooth. The sections consist of zoomorphic patterns in bold relief, repeated three times: a pair of oval eyes surrounded by broad, sharp-edged bands forming curls, hooks, and elongated curves that double back upon themselves at either end. To describe these patterns as zoomorphic is, of course, an exaggeration; but for the paired eyes there is nothing in them to suggest animal forms.

Not previously published.

This type closely resembles a *Chia* excavated at Liu-li-ko Hui-hsien, Honan (*Hui-hsien Report*, pl. 14:3; Watson, *Archaeology in China*, pl. 42), except that the decorative frieze of the latter piece is a trifle less carefully designed and is bordered by a row of circlets on top. Similar vessels were unearthed also at Cheng-chou (*KKHP*, XV, 1957/1, pl. 3:3; *Archaeology in New China*, pl. 29:2), showing large whorl circles on the "hip" in addition to the frieze around the waist.

Another close parallel is offered by a *Chia* in the Singer collection (Loehr, *Relics*, p. 37:8): its frieze is without circlets, as is the Sackler specimen's, although the composition is denser and tighter and the eyes have the same outline as those of the Brundage *Chia*, No. 4; moreover, the pillar tops of the Singer vessel are conical and are surmounted by cylindrical knobs.

9   LI
     Shang, Style II or early III
     H. 6⅜ in., w. 5⅝ in.
     Ashmolean Museum, Oxford

This tripod stands on short, slanted, tapering feet which emerge from the lobes of a body whose upper portion has an unusual form, that is, a recessed, cylindrical zone topped by a flat rim. On the rim, which is fairly broad, stand two small loop handles. The three lobes are decorated with T'ao-t'ieh faces which are confined within triangular areas centered above the feet. Their design is sharp and clear, its effect depending on the sunken curves and contours rather than on the smooth, relieved parts. The only prominent elements are the eyes, which are circular and framed in lids with short inner canthi. Interesting to note are the scalloped teeth along the inner side of the mouth. The oblique arrangement of these faces, determined by the angle of the ascending sides of the triangles, contrasts with the horizontal arrangement of the frieze above. This frieze contains three antithetical groups centered on the grooves between the lobes. Each of these is composed of a face with a low ridge between oval eyes, flanked by "bodies" executed in the same technique as the T'ao-t'ieh faces. Compared with the similar ornaments of the *Chüeh* from Seattle, No. 6, and the *Chia* of the Sackler Collections, No. 8, the Oxford *Li* ornaments are doubtless more refined; their pliant, elegant design looks toward Style III. The surface is covered by a smooth, green patina that does not detract from its metallic gloss.

　　Published: W. Watson, *Ancient Chinese Bronzes*, pl. 2 b.

Vessels of this shape, whether in bronze or in pottery, are classed as *Li* in Chinese contemporary archaeological literature; there are no compelling reasons why they should be called *Li-Ting*, let alone *Ting*. The Oxford specimen, moreover, is typologically quite early. It is not far removed from a bronze *Li* in Toronto (Stephen, "Early Chinese Bronzes," fig. 8), considered by M. Hickman as the oldest bronze type of the category in question (seminar paper, Harvard University, November 22, 1966). It stands closest to a piece excavated at Liu-li-ko, Hui-hsien, Honan, which has a similar recessed collar with an ornament in Style I (*Hui-hsien Report*, pl. 14:1; Watson, *op. cit.*, fig. 1a). The Hui-hsien piece is certainly older, however, not only by reason of its ornament but also of its doubled rim, a feature discussed apropos of the Yale *Chüeh*, No. 5. And, neither the Hui-hsien *Li* nor the Toronto *Li* is decorated with the triangular masks; their bodies are bare.

　　Comparing the Oxford *Li* with slightly later specimens of this class, we become aware of the fact that the T'ao-t'ieh does not fully cover the lobe's surface, as for instance it does in the Bluett *Li* (Karlgren, "New Studies," pl. 35:181; Loehr, "Bronze Styles," fig. 9). This modification in the Bluett vessel is accompanied by two less elusive changes: its T'ao-t'ieh is rendered by a dense maze of sunken lines, and its legs have become triangular. Still later forms of the T'ao-t'ieh are seen on vessels where the triangular section of the feet is retained, as in early Style IV pieces in the Musée Cernuschi (Loehr, "Bronze Styles," fig. 16) and in the Shanghai Museum (*Shanghai Museum Bronzes*, pl. 5), or in a late Style IV piece in the same place (*ibidem*, pl. 6).

10　CHÜEH
Shang
H. 5 ¹¹⁄₁₆ in., W. 4¾ in.
Royal Ontario Museum, Toronto

A tripod with a globular body has a spout rising at a steep angle and surmounted by a single post, a short pointed "tail," and sturdy, triangular, splayed legs. The handle issues above the central leg; forming an arc, it joins the wall below the rim. In contrast to the more primitive *Chüeh* from Yale, No. 5, the spout is broader and shaped like a U, rather than a V.

　　Published: W. C. White, *Bronze Culture of Ancient China*, pl. 79 B; Li Chi and Wan Chia-pao, *Bronze Chüeh-Cup*, p. 55, fig. 32:11.

According to White, *op. cit.*, p. 146 ff., this *Chüeh* belongs with a set of bronzes found at Tung-shih-ho-ts'un, "Eastern Stone River Village," in Hui-hsien, N. Honan, about 1946, and named by him "The Prince Kung of Sung Set," from the inscription of a *Ting* tripod (*ibid.*, pp. 150, 151). This set, however, comprises three different groups, dating from Early Chou and Shang. The *Chüeh* belongs with the third group, assigned to the Shang period, a group of vessels "most impressive in their simple dignity" (*ibid.*, p. 147). None of the four vessels—a *Ho*, a *Hu* bottle, a *Ku* beaker, and this *Chüeh* tripod—is decorated, so that they must be placed on typological grounds alone. The *Ho*, an ovoid, spouted vessel on three short, pointed feet (*ibid.*, pl. 79 A), seems to stand about midway between a Black Pottery *Ho* from Jih-chao, Shantung, and a bronze *Ho* from Hsiao-t'un, Tomb M 331, compared by Li Chi to the Neolithic piece from Jih-chao (in his "Studies of Hsiao-t'un Bronzes, Pt. I," *KKHP*, III, 1948, p. 45). The small *Hu*, a bulbous bottle with tall neck (White, pl. 80 A), a shape comparable to that of the Princeton

bottle, No. 24, but without the handle of the latter, corresponds to a type found at Hsiao-t'un in both pottery and bronze (see Li Chi, *ibid.*, pp. 58, 65). The *Ku* (White, pl. 80 B) belongs with the rather short, early forms preceding the classic late Shang designs. The group of which the *Chüeh* under discussion forms part may therefore with assurance be assigned to the earlier Anyang period at the latest.

　　It should be noted that among the *Chüeh* published in Li Chi's monograph on the vessels of this category excavated at Anyang, *Studies of the Bronze Chüeh-Cup*, there occurs not a single comparable example. One specimen of a closely comparable type, but distinguished by a small bird figure in the round placed on top of the post which rises from the bridge across the spout, is reproduced—without any indication of its provenance—in Huang Chün's *Tsun-ku-chai*, Pt. I, ch. 3 : 7; it appears also in Jung Keng's *Shang Chou i-ch'i t'ung-k'ao*, as a Shang vessel (Vol. I, p. 377, No. 23; Vol. II, fig. 437), and in Mizuno's *Bronzes and Jades of Ancient China*, pl. 18 B. Presumably this specimen is now owned by a Japanese collector.

11   HO
Shang
H. 8⅞ in., DIAM. 4½ in.
Staatliches Museum für Völkerkunde, Munich

The ovoid body of this tripod tapers toward the everted rim and is supported by triangular, gently curved and splayed pointed legs. Above one of the feet sits a sturdy handle which, forming an almost semicircular arc, joins the neck some distance below the rim, its upper part being strengthened by a slab decorated with a sunken animal mask of simple design. Opposite the handle projects a slightly curved, tubular spout whose top is level with the rim. The only decoration other than the mask on the handle consists of three widely spaced "bowstrings" around the neck. Under the handle is an inscription of one character, cast in intaglio. Its reading is in doubt. Variants are listed in Jung Keng's *Chin-wen-pien*, 1959, p. 911, without a reading. Takada (*Ku-chou-p'ien*, 1925, ch. 34: 26 b) groups the graph with the character *hsien*, "before." The same interpretation is found in Yü Hsing-wu's *Shuang-chien-i chi-chin wen-hsüan*, 1933, hsia, 3:13b–14a, s.v. *Ch'en Ho*. Lo Chen-yü took the character to mean *kuang*, "bright." More recently Yang Shu-ta (*Chi-wei-chü chin-wen-shuo*, 1959, p. 181 f.) tossed these readings out, proposing *tzu*, "son/child," instead. The vessel has a smooth, variegated light green patina.

Not previously published.

This type, which on the analogy of the *Li-Ho* (No. 7) might be called *Ting-Ho*, seems to be rare; I know of no exact parallel. A later version, however, came to the Metropolitan Museum of Art as a gift of the late Mrs. Otto H. Kahn and her children (No. 49.135.12; Lippe, "A Gift of Chinese Bronzes," p. 98f.). This is a *Ho* vessel which shows the following changes: the body is deeper; the legs, still triangular, are straight and more slender; the spout, too, is straight; the handle is rounded in cross-section and topped by a sculptured buffalo head; there is a lid with knob, linked to the handle by a short chain; and there are two décor zones of slanting, sunken S-spirals encircling the neck and the lid, respectively.

In addition, two less closely related three-legged bronze *Ho* with perfectly ovoid bodies and short, perpendicular feet should be mentioned here. One belongs with a set in the Royal Ontario Museum (No. NB.6407; White, *Bronze Cul-*

ture, pl. 79 A); it has a movable "rope" handle, not normally found in this class, and its feet are pointed. The other one was excavated at Anyang (Hsiao-t'un, M 331; Li Chi, in *KKHP*, III, 1948, p. 45, fig. 7b; *idem, The Beginnings*, pl. 45); its feet are cylindrical, and instead of either a strap-handle or a movable handle it has only two small vertical lugs. This latter vessel was compared by Li Chi to a ceramic *Ho* from a Black Pottery site in Liang-ch'eng-chen, Shantung (*KKHP*, III, 1948, p. 45, fig. 7a). Our bronze *Ho*, No. 11, agrees fairly well with this Black Pottery ceramic vessel both in shape and structure, save that the latter stands on far shorter feet. While mentioning this, I do not wish to argue that the Munich *Ho* should be placed very near the Shantung pottery jug; nonetheless it is worthy of note that its primitive character is revealed not only by the contrast to a more developed type such as the Kahn *Ho* in the Metropolitan Museum, but also by its affinity with the pre-Shang pottery piece.

12 CHÜEH
Shang, Style III
H. 7⅛ in., W. 5⅝ in.
Avery Brundage Collection, M. H. de Young Memorial Museum, San Francisco

A round vessel with rounded bottom and long, open spout, rests on three plain, triangular, pointed legs set slightly aslant. A single post, with a cap shaped as a truncated cone, rises from the transverse bar that bridges the spout. The cone is adorned with a sunken whorl ornament. The entire surface above the legs is decorated, in two superposed zones and on the under side of the spout, with proto-zoomorphic designs done, in d'Argencé's words, "in dense thread-like technique." The designs are distinguished by a fluidity and rhythmic motion that contrasts greatly with the harsher character of Style II. The form of the eyes varies with each of the three décor areas: in the lower frieze they are round, protuberant, with long inner canthi; in the upper frieze they are oval and flush with the rest; on the spout they are again round and protuberant, but the canthi are short. The handle, which, in the fashion of the archaic types, is plain, arches from the "muzzle" of the lower face to the spot between the eyes of the upper face, regardless of the ornamentation beneath. The pointed projection or "tail," to use the Chinese designation, is comparatively short, thus intensifying the asymmetry of the vessel's shape.

Published: d'Argencé, *Brundage Bronzes*, pl. VIII B.

In view of both its shape and style of decoration, this rare type must be placed later than the archaic *Chüeh* from Yale (No. 5) and from Seattle (No. 6). Still, the date suggested by d'Argencé, "13th–11th c. B.C.," may prove to be too conservative. In my estimate, a date as early as 14th–13th c. B.C. is quite likely, for evidently this type well precedes the common, standardized *Chüeh* types with tall legs, cylindrical bodies and two pillars at the spout, which constitute the bulk of this class of vessel.

13 KU
Shang, Style III
H. 8⅝₁₆ in., DIAM. 4¹⁵⁄₁₆ in.
City Art Museum of Saint Louis; gift of J. Lionberger Davis

This beaker, with slender waist and flaring mouth on a hollow, splayed foot, is similar to No. 2, but narrower at the mouth and with a decoration of later style. Here the décor covers the full height of the foot in two superposed zones, which are separated from the frieze around the waist by a ring of small circles in relief. The circlets again appear above this frieze, which is filled by two zoomorphic motifs of symmetrical design, their centers marked by low vertical ridges. In the two lower zones the motifs are repeated in succession, and are not antithetical. They are executed in crisp, relief lines forming tightly organized, pliant patterns of curves, hooks, and spirals vaguely suggestive, on account of the bulging eyes in their midst, of zoomorphic figurations. The middle zone is pierced by narrow, four-lobed, oval holes far smaller than those of the earlier *Ku* of the Royal Ontario Museum, No. 2. Inside the foot appears a pictograph of an animal in profile, hollowed out between the slightly raised outlines. The vessel is covered with a "smooth green patina with patches of malachite and cuprite" (Kidder).

Published: J. E. Kidder, Jr., *Early Chinese Bronzes in the City Art Museum of St. Louis*, p. 32, pl. 1.

Among the body of thirty-eight *Ku* illustrated in Li Chi and Wan Chia-pao, *Bronze Ku-Beaker*, pls. 6–43, excavated from Hsiao-t'un and Hou-chia-chuang sites (Anyang), there is none that quite resembles the fine specimen lent by the St. Louis Museum, none that exhibits its distinguishing feature of three registers of ornament covering foot and waist without leaving a blank space between them. This rare specimen represents an early phase of Style III; for an example of what seems to be the latest phase of Style III, the reader is referred to another, much taller *Ku* reproduced in Umehara's *Inkyo* (Yin-hsü), pl. 91.

14   CHIA
Shang, Style III
H. 13⅜ in., DIAM. 9⁹⁄₁₆ in.
City Art Museum of Saint Louis; gift of J. Lionberger Davis

The third in the sequence of Chia tripods in the exhibition, this specimen is distinguished by the following modifications: the bottom of the vessel is rounded and the abrupt break in the silhouette seen in the older shapes is avoided; the posts at the rim are heavier and larger, and they are placed diametrically; finally, the two bands of decoration are close variants in subject matter and identical in style, both exemplifying the tightly organized figurations of Style III—distinct from the airiness of Style I (No. 3) and the harshness of Style II (No. 8). The T'ao-t'ieh faces of the two bands are on the same axis, but the mouth of the upper one is formed by a double bracket while the lower, and larger, shows the innovation of fine teeth along the upper contour of the mouth, and an involute lower "jaw." The pattern is flush with the surface, and as yet there is no distinction between pattern and ground. The strap handle still resembles those of the earlier types, but there is an inscription of two sunken characters under the handle, reading: *ch'iu i*, "fermented liquor, I." Possibly the first glyph stands for *tien*, "to offer a libation." The three characters, *yu*, "spirits made from newly-ripe millet in the eighth month" (*Mathews' Dictionary*, No. 7526), *chiu*, "wine," and *ch'iu*, "fermented liquor," are close to each other in meaning, and so is the fourth one, *tien*, "a sacrifice of wine" (cf. Takada, *Ku Chou P'ien*, ch. 16:35 b). The meaning of the inscription appears to be, "for libations for (father or ancestor) I." The metal is covered by a smooth green patina, and the inside is heavily incrusted.

Published: *Bulletin*, City Art Museum of St. Louis, Vol. XXXVI/1, 1951, fig. 3; *Handbook* (of the City Art Museum of St. Louis), 1953, p. 250; Kidder, *Early Chinese Bronzes*, pl. 12.

A perfect and very tall specimen of the *Chia* of Style IV in the Freer Gallery, a type that is not represented in the exhibition, may be mentioned here to supply a telling example of the stylistic and typological advances of the stage following upon that of the St. Louis vessel. In the Freer *Chia* the low relief patterns are neatly separated from the *lei-wen* ground; the two pillars are capped by tall flaring cones; the decoration spreads to the legs as well as the flaring zone of the wall; and the sections of the zones of décor are marked by scored flanges; see Lodge, Wenley, and Pope, *Freer Gallery Bronzes*, pl. 4. But in two rectangular vessels of this class shown in the exhibition, No. 31, from the Albright-Knox Art Gallery in Buffalo, and No. 32, from the Nelson-Atkins Gallery in Kansas City, the story of the *Chia* continues through a later phase of Style IV and into Style V, respectively.

It has often been asserted that the capped posts on the rims of the *Chia* and *Chüeh* tripods served the purpose of facilitating the removal of the vessels when they had been heated over a fire. The disposition and shape of these posts in the case of the St. Louis *Chia* does not contradict that theory. But with the earlier types such as Nos. 4 and 8 in mind, where the posts are placed off center, I would rather question the soundness of the theory. The earliest *Chüeh* suggest that the raison d'être of these posts was not functional but technical.

15   P'OU
Shang, Style III
H. 9¾ in., DIAM. 14 in.
The Sackler Collections, New York City

Squat and bulbous, this round vessel, set on a low, cylindrical foot rim, has a broad, convex shoulder
and a low neck with everted lip. There are no less than four superposed bands of décor, in subtly
varied widths. Narrowest is the band on the foot rim, the design of which consists of a three-tiered
arrangement of curls around an oval eye in the center of each unit. Widest is the first frieze on the
vessel proper; in contrast to the rest of the friezes, its design is arranged symmetrically. This symmetry is established by the pair of round eyes flanking the center, which is marked by a vertical flange.
While there is as yet no coherent animal face or mask to be recognized, it is the pair of eyes that binds
the carefully organized pattern of rhythmically repeated elements together. In addition, a formation
suggestive of a mouth links the two halves of the pattern in a more factual manner. This frieze is
lined above and below by rows of circlets. The third band is similar to that on the foot; it slants
toward the left and runs on without interruption. So does the fourth, on the shoulder, where again
the protuberant eyes are at the center of rather loosely organized combinations of spirals which slant
toward the left, in units repeated without interruption. Two parallel relief lines or "strings," in
Chinese terminology, encircle the neck. All these designs are cast in low relief, from molds executed
with extreme care and assurance. One might feel that the décor, despite its relative earliness, has an air
of conventionality.

  Published: L. Katz, *Selections of Chinese Art*, catalogue of an exhibition at China House, New
York, 1967, p. 12; J. Young, *Art Styles of Ancient Shang*, No. 19.

16   YU
Shang
H. (with handle) 7⅞ in., DIAM. (at mouth) 6¼ in.
Avery Brundage Collection, M. H. de Young Memorial Museum, San Francisco

This globular jar, with contracted neck and flaring rim, handle, and foot ring, is of a completely unfamiliar type. The foot ring has the appearance of a thick, twisted rope, such as might be used to supply a stand for a round-bottomed, primitive clay pot. The handle, too, is shaped like a twisted rope; it is attached to two loops in a manner likely to limit its movement, with rings hidden underneath hollow extensions. Figures of frogs looking upward, cast half in the round, sit on top of these extensions of the arc of the handle. The vessel itself is undecorated except for three "bow strings" at the level of the loops. Inside the neck is a sunken glyph, showing a *ts'e* "document" in an oval frame surrounded by four "feet," as if to indicate a clockwise circumambulation.

Not previously published.

This vessel is an extremely interesting instance of the *Yu* type before it became standardized as a vessel of oval shape with a lid. Curiously enough the only comparable bronze *Yu*, circular like the present one, also has a "rope" handle with frog figures. It is a unique specimen in the collection of the Marchese Taliani di Marchio, Rome (cf. *Yeh-chung p'ien-yü*, III, shang, 31). It differs from the Brundage piece on four counts, all of them suggesting a still earlier date for the latter: (1) the rope ring is replaced by a cylindrical ring decorated with sunken spirals; (2) the vessel tapers evenly toward the rim, which does not flare; (3) a frieze with Style II ornaments replaces the "bow strings"; and (4) the handle forms a taller arc and is twisted more tightly and neatly. Be that as it may, these two *Yu* appear to antedate all the rest of the now known specimens of this class. Their claim to relative earliness is further supported by the fact that neither of the two is likely to have had a lid, to judge from the shape of the rims as well as from the position of the handles. Contrariwise, the style of the décor of the Taliani *Yu* and the degree of technical sophistication revealed by the fact that both have cast handles supply sufficient evidence to exclude a date as early as that of a truly primitive bronze such as the tumbler of the Ashmolean Museum, No. 1.

If, for want of comparable shapes among the bronzes, we turn toward Shang pottery, we find tolerably close parallels among the wares excavated at Erh-li-kang, Cheng-chou (*KKHP*, XV, 1957/1, Table 1; *Cheng-chou Erh-li-kang*, drawings, pls. 10:3, 11:4), and at least one from Anyang (Dexel, *Die Formen chinesischer Keramik*, pl. 14a), and the globular bottoms of these wares confirm our inference made from the rope-like foot ring of the bronze.

The conspicuous motif of the frog appeared well before Shang; in fact, the frog may be about the earliest of the animal motifs encountered in Chinese art, appearing as it does in the painted décor of late Neolithic pottery (Ma-chia-yao, Kansu: Sommarström, in *BMFEA*, XXVIII, 1956, pl. 60:5, figs. 8, 9; Chêng Tê-k'un, *Prehistoric China*, pl. 24:2 b; Miao-ti-kou, Honan: *Miao-ti-kou Monograph*, pl. 9:1–3). For Shang, Chêng Tê-k'un assumes the frog to have been one of the four most frequently represented animals: the buffalo, the frog, the tiger, and the bear (*Shang China*, p. 108). One of the Shang royal tombs at Hou-chia-chuang contained a beautifully carved stone frog in the round covered with spiral designs (Li Chi, *The Beginnings*, pl. 25; *HPKM 1001*, Vol. II, pl. 94:3,

drawings, pl. 97), a piece whose very origin and exquisite design testify to the importance of the motif. Other frog sculptures to mention are a jade carving owned by Professor Chêng Tê-k'un (*Shang China*, pl. 17 b) and an extraordinary, large marble frog of cubistic form in the R. C. Bull collection (Fong Chow, *Animals and Birds in Chinese Art*, catalogue of an exhibition at China House, New York, 1967, No. 1) that was taken by Salmony to be older than Anyang (*AA*, XX/4, 1957, p. 239).

In mythology and folklore, frog, toad, and turtle are not strictly distinguished. There exists a three-legged turtle as well as a three-legged toad, which is a moon symbol *par excellence*. The frog partakes of their magical powers. One of man's two souls, *hun*, the dark one, looks exactly like a frog. Frogs can change into quails, their solar opposites (*MoTi*, tr. A. Forke, 1922, p. 449). Frog cults and a frog deity were traced by Eberhard in Kiangsi and Chekiang (W. Eberhard, *Die Lokalkulturen des Südens und Ostens*, 1942, pp. 184–186, 195–199), who mentions that, according to Ch'en Meng-chia (*Yenching Journal*, XX, 1936, p. 519), there may have been a sacrifice connected with frogs in Shang times. The nature of this sacrifice is not known; conceivably it was a rain sacrifice.

On bronze vessels the frog is seldom represented. One case is a *P'ou* from the collection of Mrs. Christian R. Holmes (Umehara, *Seika*, II, 126; Jung Keng, *Shang Chou*, fig. 896), where frogs in the round sit radially on the shoulder of the vessel, which in addition is decorated with a band of fish in low relief. This *P'ou*, regarded as a Shang bronze by Jung Keng, seems to be the only instance of the use of quite similar sculptural frog figures. Its design, however, is suggestive of a provenance other than Anyang. A *P'an* showing a frog in the round in the center, possibly of late Western Chou date, is in the Sumitomo collection (*Senoku Seishō*, revised ed., 1934, pl. 34, No. 127; *Shang Chou*, fig. 830). In the superb Warring States oval basin with two full-round frogs jumping from the rim, formerly in the Holmes collection, now in the Sackler Collections (Umehara, *Seika*, III, 210; *Shang Chou*, fig. 924), the somber aspect of a magical or ritualistic purpose gives way to secular elegance and charm. The only example of a whole vessel shaped as a frog is a bronze in the W. van der Mandele collection, Bloemendaal, Holland (H. F. E. Visser, *Asiatic Art*, 1948, pl. 32, No. 31), a vessel sculpture which in its powerful, summary modeling seems like a descendant of the marble frog in the Bull collection mentioned above.

17 HU
Shang, Style IV
H. 13¾ in., w. 9¾ in.
The Sackler Collections, New York City

The body of this exquisitely shaped, tall vase of tin-colored metal is oval in cross-section, its wide sides flattened. Rising from a conical foot, the wall projects energetically, tapering off in a slightly concave silhouette until it reaches the topmost zone, which gently flares out again. Two vertical lugs, level with the lower edge of this plain zone, repeat inversely and in small scale both the taper and the curve of the wall. The lugs are fashioned into animal heads with large, protuberant, round eyes. The vessel is decorated with five superposed zones of ornament. With the exception of a narrow band of barbed S spirals in alternating positions, crisply done in intaglio, the ornament is characterized by a technical differentiation between pattern proper and ground. Broad lines and widely spaced spirals on the wider bands read as pattern, while small and exceedingly fine spirals and striae filling the interstices read as ground. The dominating motifs are two faces centered on the wide sides of the vessel, their scale differing in accordance with the given width of the surface. Their eyes are spherical and without indications of pupils; they are placed near the outer corners of the framing contours with their long, hooked, inner canthi. Both faces are marked by strong vertical ribs emphasizing the common axis, and both exhibit the same kind of mouth—if, indeed, the parallel stripes and small pendant hooks below the eyes may be called a mouth. Their designs are similar as to the appendages to the left and right of the eyes, but distinct as to the forms of the "horns": the lower face has the horns turned inward, the upper one, outward. A narrow band separates the faces just described. It is occupied by "monoculi" with long arms that are formed by double stripes ending in hooks, which point upward at the left end, downward at the right end. The same motif is used in the narrow band at the foot rim. These bands, like the top frieze of S spirals, do not participate in the axial order of the fronting, static faces. Some of the patterns rise above the surrounding, finely cast *lei-wen* ground, while others are flush with the adjoining ground. It is possible that the process of oxidation brought about some of the uneven elevations; but, from the beginning, there may have been a relief formed in a manner curiously lacking uniformity. The last feature to mention is the simple raised lines above the uppermost frieze, the "strings" of Chinese terminology, which run horizontally between the lugs.

Not previously published.

A detail that must not pass unnoticed is the formation of the fine *lei-wen* ground. It is by no means a uniformly treated, featureless device merely serving as background or as a contrasting texture. On the contrary, there is much variety of form and position in these spirals and striations, which on close examination reveal their origin: they are miniaturized elements of Style III. Hence they are symptomatic of the relative earliness of the design and, consequently, of the date of this vessel. In later works, the *lei-wen* becomes quite uniform, as for instance in the imposing *Hu* from Kansas City, No. 33. In principle, therefore this inconspicuous element called "thunder pattern" can contribute to our understanding of its historical position.

The stylistic position of the Sackler *Hu* is fairly unmistakable. It represents an early phase of Style IV, still close to Style III as represented by a magnificent specimen in the Östasiatiska Museet, Stockholm, which unfortunately is too brittle to permit its traveling to New York. The reader, therefore, is referred to the illustrations in Karlgren's "New Studies," pl. 48:628; Karlgren's "Some Bronzes in the M.F.E.A.," pl. 16, and Loehr's "Bronze Styles," fig. 10. In the Stockholm *Hu* the arrangement of four ornamental zones is similar, including two zones with faces, while there is as yet no breaking up of the unified relief pattern into "pattern" and "ground." A later phase of Style IV is exemplified by a *Hu* from Anyang with six zones of décor (Loehr, "Bronze Styles," fig. 13). Style V, however, appears in what I take to be an early instance in the Kansas City *Hu* shown in this exhibition, No. 33.

18 P'OU
Shang, Style IV
H. 5 ¾ in., DIAM. 10 in.
Avery Brundage Collection, M. H. de Young Memorial Museum, San Francisco

This squat vessel with expansively bulging wall and accordingly wide, sloping shoulder, with a low neck and everted lip, is of the type described under No. 15 above. The slightly conical foot is decorated with a band of barbed spirals in flat relief; the spirals, slanting to the left, form the ends of horizontal strips in alternating position, so that they bracket the two spiral ends of the adjacent strips. The main frieze is divided into three sections, each of which is occupied by symmetrical, geometric assemblages of lines and curves on both sides of a face with protuberant, round eyes. The flat lineament stands out clearly from the ground pattern formed by a maze of fine, small spirals. Down the middle of each face runs a strong ridge. To the left and right of the mouth, which has the same form as seen in the *P'ou*, No. 15, and the *Hu*, No. 17, we notice a claw in flat relief, undoubtedly the precursor of the formidable claws in high relief as seen in the Kansas City *Hu*, No. 33, which is of later style. In the frieze on the shoulder appear "dragon" figures whose heads point to the right, without symmetrical confrontation and without regard to the axes of the three faces in the main frieze. The neck is plain, except for a simple "string" line encircling it.

Published: d'Argencé, *Brundage Bronzes*, pl. XIV A; Loehr, "Bronze Styles," fig. 14.

19   P'OU
     Shang, Style IV
     H. 6½ in., DIAM. 8½ in.
     The Detroit Institute of Arts; gift of Allan Gerdau

A squat bowl with steep sides, sloping and convex shoulder, contracted, low neck and slightly flaring rim, is similar to No. 15 but has a relatively high conical foot. The decoration is executed in intaglio; only the eyes of the zoomorphic designs stand out in relief. The effect of the designs is heightened by a blackish filling of the grooves, which are dense in the angular meander pattern of the ground but sparse within the figures proper. The figures, therefore, contrast as coherent, light bodies with the more or less evenly dark ground. The widest zone is given to the configuration known as T'ao-t'ieh, which is repeated three times. The emergence of this motif from stylistically earlier stages can be followed, within the *P'ou* category, if we compare the present version with the numbers 15 and 18. Particularly instructive, aside from the overall changes, are the formulations of details such as the mouth, or the claws, or the horns. Another telling trait in this series is the gradual elimination of the "quills," of which there is only one left in the design of the Detroit piece. In the shoulder zone there are strange, quasi-zoomorphic elements lined up, all moving to the left in disregard of the axes of the T'ao-t'ieh below them. These elements are most interesting. They are the results, somewhat random results we might say, of the technical innovations seen in the decorative design at large and now applied to the still inarticulate, pleasingly ambiguous and unobtrusive spirals, large and small, such as may be seen in the *P'ou* from the Sackler Collections, No. 15, in the same zone. Above this zone runs a border of small, relief circles, while the neck is surrounded by two "bowstrings." On the foot we find a belt filled with a purely geometric ornament: elongated S-curved bands with single hooks or barbs pointing upward and downward, respectively, and framed by rectangular meanders. Above the ornament the wall of the foot is pierced by four shapeless holes.

Not previously published.

20   TING
Shang, Style IV
H. 5⅜ in., DIAM. 5⁹⁄₁₆ in.
Nelson-Atkins Gallery, Kansas City, Mo. (Nelson Fund)

This tripod with a deep, round body is supported by sturdy, cylindrical legs placed in nearly per-pendicular position. The décor, a perfect example of the developed Style IV, consists of two friezes with common axes, which are marked by low vertical ridges. The lower and wider frieze is filled by three T'ao-t'ieh with long, lateral bodies. The formation of their "horns" appears to be prefigured in a Style III design such as that on the *P'ou* of the Sackler Collections, No. 15; the mouth, on the other hand, still similar to older conventions in its broad middle part, shows a novel formation in its short inward-curled corners, a formation somewhat comparable to that of the lower T'ao-t'ieh on the *Chia* from St. Louis, No. 14, which is a late Style III specimen. In the narrow, upper frieze we find two pairs of small dragons above each T'ao-t'ieh, repeated three times. Their bodies echo the form of the T'ao-t'ieh horns; they have large eyes and fine teeth. "The design is now presented with great lucidity. By reducing in size the meanders of the background, and by spacing widely those in the interior of the animals, the main themes stand out very clearly," wrote Bachhofer of this *Ting.* The meanders or ground spirals are formed with admirable precision and in such variations that they seem an active part of the decoration, rather than a neutral and even pattern. The feet, too, are deco-rated with spirals, but their effect is obliterated by corrosion. As in the case of the small *Ting* from Princeton, No. 22, and the *Li-Ting* of the Victoria & Albert Museum, No. 26, the sunken parts of the décor are filled with a black paste, which effectively contrasts with the green, patinated surface.

    Published: L. Bachhofer, *A Short History*, fig. 11; L. Sickman, *Early Chinese Art*, University Prints, O92; *Chinese Bronzes*, catalogue of the Metropolitan Museum exhibition, 1934, No. 19; F. Waterbury, *Early Chinese Symbols and Literature*, pl. 37.

21 LI-TING
Shang
H. 5 ⅞ in., DIAM. 5 ½ in.
Avery Brundage Collection, M. H. de Young Memorial Museum, San Francisco

The bottom of this tripod, consisting of a round bowl shaped like a *Li*, slopes from the center toward three cavities. Three comparatively short and thin cylindrical legs, placed in nearly vertical position, are joined to the body below those cavities. The wall is slightly convex. It is topped by a strong rim from which two loop handles rise. The decoration is restricted to the bowl and harmonizes with its shape. Plain stripes, separated by bands of rectangular spirals, descend from the upper edge in accordance with the slope of the bottom, forming a slow-moving, zigzag pattern all around the sides. The spirals, or meanders, are cast with unbelievable fineness and density. Above this pattern runs a frieze with a very simple but also very rarely encountered motif: in rectangles, slanting slightly to the left side and endlessly repeated, there appear sunken figures of parallel lines ending in a hook at the right and a curl at the left above, and in reverse and inverted position below.

The vessel bears an inscription of one glyph, combining a cross sign or *ya-hsing* with the pictograph of a man, that is, the primitive form of the character *fu*, "man," which often is indistinguishable from the primitive form of *t'ien*, "heaven." Possibly this glyph is an abbreviated version of the more complex one in the *Fang I* from Cincinnati, No. 38.

Not previously published.

The only closely comparable vessel, formerly in Anders Hellström's collection, is in the Östasiatiska Museet in Stockholm (*Catalogue of the International Exhibition of Chinese Art at the Royal Academy of Arts*, London, 1935–36, No. 251; Loehr, "Beiträge zur Chronologie der älteren chinesischen Bronzen," *Ostasiatische Zeitschrift*, N.F. XII, 1936, pl. 2:1; Karlgren, "Marginalia," *BMFEA*, XXXI, 1959, pl. 60b). Its décor combines a more briskly moving zigzag with a frieze of sunken S spirals very like those on a *Hu* from the Sackler Collections, No. 17. The rare design of the frieze on the Brundage *Li-Ting* appears on the foot rim of an early, round *Yu* in the collection of Marchese Taliani di Marchio, Rome (see *Yeh-chung p'ien-yü*, Pt. III, shang, 31). The Taliani *Yu*, whose main frieze represents a highly archaic phase of protozoomorphic design, may in turn be compared with a round *Yu* from the Avery Brundage Collection, No. 16. While these analogies furnish no precise date, they do suggest a rather early phase, as vouched for also by the shape of the vessel. A glance at the typologically related tripod of Style IV, lent by the Victoria & Albert Museum, No. 26, reveals the changed, sturdier proportions of the *Li-Ting* of the developed Style IV. There can be no doubt about the greater antiquity of the Brundage piece.

22 TING
Shang, Style IV(?)
H. 7⅝ in., DIAM. 6 in.
The Art Museum, Princeton University

The bowl of this small tripod is supported by straight, cylindrical and rather sturdy legs. Upright loop handles rise vertically from the strengthened rim. The décor consists of one frieze below the rim. It is filled with whorl roundels alternating with a motif named "squares with crescents" in Karlgren's terminology, and it is bordered by rows of circlets above and below. Except for the whorls, the design is flush with the vessel surface. The sunken parts of the design are filled with a black substance, even now producing a clear contrast to the mat green, oxidized metal.

Not previously published.

A close parallel to this rare type is a *Ting* in an unnamed private collection illustrated in two of Karlgren's papers, "New Studies" and "Marginalia." The shape is approximately the same as that of the Princeton specimen, but there is a small difference in respect of the role accorded to the *lei-wen* which, there, fills not only the spaces between a roundel and the "square" next to it, but also the bays of the crescents.

To consider the "square with crescents" as a "corrupted remnant of a Dragon figure," as did Karlgren ("Marginalia," p. 327), is erroneous. All that this motif has in common with Dragons is the eye. The motif occurs—associated with the whorl—as early as the Erh-li-kang phase, in a form that excludes the possibility of its derivation from Dragons; see the reproductions of a pottery sherd from Erh-li-kang, one of the Cheng-chou sites, in "Excavations at Cheng-chou" (*KKHP*, XV, 1957, p. 68, fig. 13:11); *Cheng-chou Erh-li-kang*, 1959 (rubbing, pl. 31:9; photo, pl. 13:3); Soper, "Early, Middle, and Late Shang," fig. 10:3.

23 YÜ
Shang, Style IV
H. 5⅝ in., DIAM. 8¼ in.
Musée Cernuschi, Paris

A bowl of slightly expanding profile, with strengthened lip, stands on a contracted, conical foot without molding. A vessel of great simplicity and an archaic air, it is decorated with much restraint. Around the foot runs a belt with a continuous pattern of whorl medallions alternating with eyed stars, or "squares with crescents" in Karlgren's terminology, executed in sunken outlines on a ground of spirals and elongated meanders. The same technique is used in the belt around the neck which, in contrast to the lower belt, is divided into three sections. Each of these sections is filled with six cicada figures in horizontal position; in antithetical groups of three they face toward the center that is marked by a small animal head with ram's horns modeled in relief. There are no flanges to stress the sections of this band. The upper part of the foot, above the décor, is pierced by small rectangular holes, located in accordance with the three divisions of the upper belt. The patina is light green.

Not previously published.

The shape of this rare specimen occurs among the ceramics excavated by the Academia Sinica at Anyang; Umehara, *Inkyo* (Yin-hsü), pl. 48:2, reproduces a comparable ceramic bowl without décor, rightly adopting the designation *Yü*, rather than *Kuei*, a designation discussed under No. 35 below. Similar ceramic types excavated at Cheng-chou (*KKHP*, XV, 1957/1, p. 63, fig. 7) speak for a greater antiquity of this type than is established by the Anyang finds alone. Judged by the far more common bronze *Kuei* with its vertical handles, the Cernuschi *Yü* quite obviously shows a greater resemblance to the pottery types. Among typical late Shang bronzes it looks lost and foreign. Still, *Kuei* closely related in the shapes of their bowls, but with handles, do exist in bronze. Two of these bronzes, moreover, are decorated in the same sparse manner and with the same ornaments, eyed stars in one case, and eyed stars with whorl medallions in the other case (Jung Keng, *Shang Chou*, II, figs. 222, 223). Two vessels without handles, classed as *Kuei* in Jung Keng's

corpus, offer particularly close parallels among the bronzes of this type (*ibid.*, figs. 235, 236; the former also *Tsun-ku-chai*, 1:38).

There are three vessels of this class among the exhibits here assembled (Nos. 23, 35, 36). Comparing their shapes we soon become aware of their relative positions: the Cernuschi piece is the earliest among them. This conclusion is confirmed by the style of the décor of these three *Yü*.

The feature of the "three openings in the foot collar, of unknown use," was tentatively explained by Karlgren as "vents for fumes from charcoal" in his description of a related type of bowl without handles in the collection of Dr. N. D. T. Wessén ("Wessén Collection," p. 182, pl. 15). It is a type that shares the decorative restraint and the simple conical foot with the vessels mentioned above, but its wall is almost semispherical. Its ornaments, not too felicitously interpreted (*ibid.*, p. 183, figs. a–d), agree with Style IV.

24 HU WITH HANDLE
Shang
H. (including handle) 12⅜ in., DIAM. 5⁵⁄₁₆ in.
The Art Museum, Princeton University

This graceful, pear-shaped flask, on a conical foot, has a long, flaring neck and a domed lid sur-mounted by a knob. A large swing-handle that follows the contour of the vessel up to the mouth, then widens to form an approximately semicircular arch, is linked to the lid by a short chain attached to the knob and to a small loop on the handle. The handle is rectangular in cross-section and shaped so as to suggest the body of a snake, which is marked by a continuous chain of boxed rhombi and terminates in triangular heads on the broadened ends. The snake heads hide the device to which the handle is affixed. The decoration is exceedingly sparing. Narrow bands of beautifully drawn spirals with barbs encircle the foot and the lid; another such band borders the upper edge of an unusually narrow T'ao-t'ieh frieze, the formation of which seems to presuppose the stage of Style III. The patina is glossy black and turquoise-greenish.

Published: Umehara, *Nihon Seika*, pl. 47; N. Barnard, *Bronze Casting and Bronze Alloys*, color frontispiece.

Apparently this slender-bodied type of container with bail, or elongated, semi-circular handle, is rather rare. I am unable to adduce an exactly similar specimen, but a slightly stockier type of less elegant proportions in the Hellström collection, provided with the same snake-body handle and comparable décor, should be mentioned (*Yeh-chung p'ien-yü*, Pt. III, shang, 33b; Karlgren, "Hellström Collection," pl. 15:1); the decoration of the lid of this piece, a dragon curled so as to fill the round surface, appears to be of Style IV. A specimen in the H. J. v. Lochow collection compares well in its proportions and sparse ornament. It has a late Style III T'ao-t'ieh at the neck combined with simple spiral bands at the foot and on the lid, but its handle shows a flange with deep notches and animal heads with bottle horns (*Sammlung Lochow*, II, 10; Consten, *Das alte China*, pl. 16 right). The features of the scored flange and the bottle-horn animal heads on the handle tie the Lochow example to a type which is distinguished by the fact of its decoration covering the entire surface—a vessel in the Brundage collection with flat relief ornaments of Style IV, arranged in no less than seven superposed friezes on the body and two additional bands on the lid (Umehara, *Inkyo*, pl. 102; d'Argencé, *Brundage Bronzes*, pl. 16; Karlgren, "Some Characteristics," pl. 56A). One last example

I wish to mention of the type with flanged bail terminated by bottle-horn heads is a vessel in an unnamed collection published by Mizuno (*Bronzes and Jades*, pl. 47); its décor atypically associates elements of Style IV with boldly relieved horns of Style V, above which are arrayed hooked quills derived from Style III. Without taking the variant with square body into account, I believe that the several examples described above warrant placing the Princeton piece earlier than the fully developed Style IV.

The excavations at Anyang brought one such vessel with overall decorated surface to light (Hsiao-t'un, M 238; Li Chi, in *KKHP*, III, 1948, pl. 8:2a–c). The same shape occurs in pottery, though without the handle (Umehara, *Inkyo*, pl. 53:2).

Despite the identity of their shapes, the bail-handled type of vessel is called *Yu*, while that without handle is called *Hu*. The shape of the common *Yu*, however, is so clearly distinct from the *Hu* that it must seem contradictory to apply the designation, *Yu* to the *Hu* types, even though they may have handles. To avoid an awkward binomial term such as *Hu-Yu* or "*Hu*-shaped wine jug with handle," I beg leave for using the designation chosen, "*Hu* with handle," for this vessel from Princeton.

25 CHIH
Shang, Style IV
H. 6¼ in., W. 5 in.
Mr. John M. Crawford, Jr., New York City

In this oval beaker with a low ring-foot, and a domed lid surmounted by a conical knob, the wall contracts somewhat below the rim, then swells moderately. The foot is strongly recessed. The vessel is decorated with four horizontal friezes. Two of these are bands of roundish, barbed spirals leaning to the left side and moving continuously, without reference to the central ridges marking the T'ao-t'ieh formations in the main frieze and on the lid. These T'ao-t'ieh, executed like the rest of the ornaments in flat relief, are centered on the wide sides of the goblet. Their eyes are the only parts in high relief; they are outlined by contours forming very long inner canthi with sharply recurved corners. Beneath each eye are two large spirals, just above the double line which encloses the area between the eyes and ends in short, pointed curls. Bands on the outer sides of the eyes are filled with spirals, like those in the narrow bands above and below the T'ao-t'ieh. The spirals of the ground pattern, by contrast, are angular and small. The horns are broad and rolled inward; they are marked with scores along the outer contour and with hooks and spirals within. Beyond these horns rise two broad, knife-shaped blades or quills, filling the spaces between the horns and the tails, the interiors of which are marked with the same linear combinations seen in the horns. Below the blades or quills there are small claws. The T'ao-t'ieh on the lid are similar but modified, or abbreviated, in accordance with the more limited space. In the topmost, flaring zone, under the rim, the ornament consists of a row of triangles with geometric, incised patterns, contrasting with the plain interstices. On the knob we find the common, whorl circle. The metal surface has a smooth, olive-green and russet patina.

Published: J. Young, *Art Styles of Ancient Shang*, fig. 18.

A similar but taller beaker of this class, also with a lid, is in the Minneapolis Institute of Arts (Karlgren, *Pillsbury Collection*, No. 30). Its décor, in the flat relief on angular meander ground of Style IV, represents a more advanced stage than the Crawford specimen. The unambiguous and telling differences are these: symmetry rules in all of the registers of ornamentation; the T'ao-t'ieh is clarified by the elimination of the quill and, particularly, by the formation of the jaws; the "shield" in the middle is transformed into a large, coherent unit; the interior design of the horns is streamlined to agree with the contours; and the knob on the lid is given a tectiform shape. Even the form of the eyes is affected by the tendency toward simplification. Only the claws are virtually unchanged. Within the range of Style IV, therefore, the Crawford *Chih* precedes the Pillsbury *Chih*, which nonetheless is still of Shang date.

If, apropos of the clarified relationship of these two vessels, an attempt be made to extend our findings to other Style IV designs of the T'ao-t'ieh on bronzes in this exhibition, the following sequence would seem plausible: Sackler *Hu*, No. 17—Crawford *Chih*, No. 25—Detroit *P'ou*, No. 19—Victoria & Albert *Li-Ting*, No. 26, with eyes as in the preceding cases, but with jaws like those of the Pillsbury *Chih* mentioned above.

26   LI-TING
     Shang, Style IV
     H. 7½ in., DIAM. 6¼ in.
     Victoria & Albert Museum, London

This tripod is of the same type as No. 21, but larger, of heavier proportions, and decorated with zoomorphic designs in a style closer to the classic Shang style. There is no relief except for the round eyes, which have no pupils. The rest of the design is executed in sunken lines that are made to contrast with the surface of the bronze by a black filling. The main motif is a large T'ao-t'ieh which, centered on the bulges of the tripartite body, recurs three times. Its forms appear light against the darker ground because they are defined by fewer lines and wider spirals than are found in the ground pattern of rectangular spirals. Measured by the complexity and profusion of elements in characteristic instances of Style III and earlier IV, these masks are distinguished by clarity and compactness. As in the *Li-Ting* No. 21, the areas of decoration narrow as they recede from the bulges toward the three constrictions of the body. Remarkable features of the masks are the straight edges uniting the eyes with the lateral extensions or "bodies" of the T'ao-t'ieh, and the large blank areas of the inner canthi, which, in a most unusual manner, are broken at right angles at the lower corners. The frieze above is occupied by cicadas placed sideways and facing away from the center of each mask, four in each section.

   Not previously published.

There exist several *Li-Ting* of similar shape with similar decoration: *Yeh-chung p'ien-yü* (Pt. III, shang, 9), with large cicada figures on the legs; Kidder, *Early Chinese Bronzes*, pl. 7, with pupils in the eyes of both the T'ao-t'ieh and the cicadas; Karlgren, "Marginalia," pl. 22b, illustrating a specimen from the Ernest Erickson collection with the T'ao-t'ieh flanked by bird figures and the cicadas facing toward the center rather than outward. This last specimen I believe to be the latest in this group, and the Victoria & Albert piece the earliest.

27　KUAN OR YU
Shang, Style IV
H. 7 in., W. (at mouth) 8 in.
Honolulu Academy of Arts; Wilhelmina Tenney Memorial Collection

An exceedingly rare type of oval, squat container has a recessed, plain collar which indicates that originally it was covered with a lid. A vessel with bulging sides and contracted neck, it stands on a fairly high ring-foot without a molding. At the narrow sides, level with the upper border of the neck belt, there are two vertical lugs which must have served to secure the lid to the body of the vessel. The décor is arranged in three registers, harmonizing with the structure. The designs of all three are centered on the sides. Lowermost, we find a mask with slightly protuberant, oval eyes surrounded by barbed spirals, and with a strong ridge down the middle; to the left and right of the eyes are parallel bands ending in hooks and volutes, respectively, and set off against the ground pattern of fine, neatly drawn, squarish spirals. The much wider frieze on the belly is occupied by four T'ao-t'ieh faces with round eyes, framed in hooked lid contours, within a plain area that binds the features together as a mask. The jaws are large and involute. Adjoining the eyes and separating them from the body bands on the sides are pointed ears, filled with small spirals. The horns, too, are partly filled with spirals; rendered in two distinct sections, the inner one forms a scored frame with an obtuse end, the frame that encloses the spirals, while the outer one forms a sharply pointed hook with grooves running lengthwise. Clawed feet appear under the body bands. The outer corners of each T'ao-t'ieh unit accommodate small figures of dragons plunging headlong. All these designs are flush with the ground, which is covered by fine, rounded spirals that are as large as a given space permits. Finally, in the uppermost zone, the center is occupied by a large Tiger head in high relief with incised features. On both sides of the head are drawn the profile views of the Tiger's body, scored along the undulating back, marked with "scales" throughout its length from the neck to the tail, and provided with big claws like those of the T'ao-t'ieh. The lugs at the narrow sides function similarly as the heads of the adjoining Tiger bodies. While strongly corroded in part, the vessel still displays its magnificent ornamentation almost unimpaired.

Published: Karlgren, in *BMFEA*, XXXI, 1959, pl. 73 b (the indication of the Seattle Art Museum as owner appears to be an error).

A perfect example of the developed Style IV, this vessel appears to be a unique specimen as far as its shape is concerned. Umehara's *Kodōki keitai* does not contain this type. One bronze of comparable structure but different shape is reproduced in Jung Keng's *Sung-chai, hsü*, shang, 53 (cf. *idem, Shang Chou*, fig. 645). It is a footed bowl with two lugs and a lid that completes the nearly globular outline; its décor consists of two bands showing dragons at the foot, similar to the Honolulu vessel, and whorl medallions alternating with eyed stars, similar to the frieze of the Princeton *Ting*, No. 22. Jung Keng designates the type as *Yu*. Only once did I see another specimen of the same type in Peking, which was decorated with a very shallow cast T-hook pattern all over the surface. Among the Academia Sinica finds of Shang glazed pottery another relevant example occurs, of squat globular shape, with two pairs of lugs, complete with lid (Umehara, *Inkyo*, pl 58:3), a lidded bowl which Umehara

unexpectedly designates as *Hu*. A closely similar, glazed pottery bowl, distinguished, like the last example, by double sets of lugs and by an unusually large conical foot, is in the collection of the Royal Ontario Museum in Toronto; its lid is missing, but a recessed, straight collar shows that it was made to receive a lid (Dexel, *Formen*, pl. 11B). Chêng Tê-k'un, *Shang China*, pl. 30B, applies the term *Kuan* to this vessel, following contemporary usage in the nomenclature of pottery.

The motif of the Tiger represented with a scored flange at the back and a combination of "scales" and other motifs on the body appears among the superb bone carvings excavated from the large Tomb 1001 at Hsi-pei-kang near Hou-chia-chuang, one of the Anyang sites (*HPKM* 1001, Pt. 2, pl. 212: 2, 3, 5, 7). Both flanges and scales occur, also, on fantastic beasts such as antlered dragons (*ibidem*, pl. 210:8, 9). For discussions of the "scale" sign, see Karlgren, in *BMFEA*, XXIV, 1952, 17–23, and XXXI, 1959, 320.

28 P'AN
Shang, Style IV
H. 3¼ in., DIAM. 13¼ in.
Mr. and Mrs. Frederick M. Mayer, New York City

A large, shallow bowl with curved sides and flat rim rests on a conical ring-foot. The rich décor of the interior is dominated by the large and impressive face of a coiled snake, a face which, in its pure frontality and hypnotic stare, has an almost demonic power. The round, protruding eyes with sunken pupils, the ears, and a diamond on the forehead do not differ from those in the T'ao-t'ieh designs; the mushroom horns, on the other hand, as well as the nose and the outline of this face from ear to ear are not found in T'ao-t'ieh faces. The snake's body is marked by a pattern of small scales, plain ones alternating with scales showing boxed contours, and this patterned body is lined on both sides with scored flanges—comparable to the flange on the Tigers' bodies in the preceding vessel, No. 27. Enclosed in the coil, above the right horn, is a small dragon-like creature rendered in profile view, and in outlines only. On the wall of the vessel, surrounding the snake demon, is a continuous row of small snakes. Their bodies, also marked by scales, are far from serpentine in outline; identical in form, the bodies change directions at right angles three times, so that a curve appears only at the tails. Twelve in all, they show in alternate order two kinds of horns—bovine, and mushroom or bottle-shaped. Above the ears of the big snake are two sunken glyphs, the meaning of which remains to be determined. The metal has acquired a shiny dark green surface.

Not previously published.

Among the few *P'an* basins of comparable decoration, none approaches this magnificent specimen as closely as does that in the Trautmann collection (G. Ecke, *Sammlung Oskar Trautmann*, 17; Jung Keng, *Shang Chou*, fig. 823). It is slightly smaller, and its design slightly simpler; there is no dragon figure inserted within the coil of the snake's body, which is covered with the same pattern of small scales. The main difference lies in the animal figures encircling the snake: instead of snakes we see in succession a fish, a bird, a tiger, all moving to the right, three times repeated in this order. The supposed Anyang provenance of the Trautmann *P'an* is accepted by Umehara, who included it in his Yin-hsü book, *Inkyo* (pl. 81), under the name of a Japanese collector who once owned it.

A third piece to mention is in the British Museum (Watson, *Ancient Chinese Bronzes*, pl. 26A,B), which, by reason of its exterior décor, would also belong in the range of Style IV; its snake, however, while similar in regard to the coiled position, has a body covered by only two rows of scales of uniform design. The face of the snake is more angular, and two details suggest a later date than that of the preceding piece as well as of the Mayer *P'an*, No. 28: above the eyes are striated eyebrows, and the ears have the form commonly seen in late Shang bronzes. The face, moreover, is surrounded by a dragon, two tiny tigers, two fish, and two snakes. An inscription of three characters is placed in the center of the snake's face. The British Museum *P'an* appears to be identical with the specimen illustrated in Chêng Tê-k'un's *Shang China*, pl. 56B.

There is an extraordinarily fine *P'an* with a big snake in the collection of the Hakuzuru Museum (*Hakkaku*, No. 21) which is clearly related to the British Museum piece, but differs widely both technically and stylistically. It also shows the fish-bird-tiger procession, but the forms seem to be Chou rather than Shang, as rightly recognized in Mizuno's *Bronzes and Jades*, pl. 120, where this piece is illustrated side by side with a very similar type with a more plastically conceived snake, found at Lo-yang (*op. cit.*, pl. 121). A late Western Chou date applies also in the case of yet another *P'an* with a big snake head as decorative device and obviously derived from such types as the Hakuzuru and Lo-yang pieces. It is a *P'an* excavated in an ancient cemetery of the Kuo State at Shang-ts'un-ling, N.W. Honan, in 1956–57, the inventory of which cemetery antedates the year 655 B.C., when Kuo was annexed by the State of Chin (*Shang-ts'un-ling Report*, pl. 18).

29   TSUN

Shang, Style IV

H. 15⅝ in., DIAM. (at mouth) 14 in.

The Metropolitan Museum of Art, New York City; Rogers Fund, 1943

This tall and stately vessel is built up in three horizontal sections. The foot, which is hollow and unusually high, has the shape of a truncated cone. It supports a body that widens toward its sharply angled shoulder, which, in an almost imperceptibly convex, inward slope, springs back to the same diameter as that of the body's base. From this shoulder rises the magnificently flaring neck with trumpet-shaped mouth, whose width by far exceeds that of the shoulder. The decoration accords with the clear articulation of the vessel's parts. A wide band on the foot shows T'ao-t'ieh designs, characterized by tall, pointed horns adapted to fill the given space, a mouth with teeth and small fangs, and claws turned outward. On the body proper are two friezes; the lower, wider one again shows T'ao-t'ieh images, with jaws rolled inward, claws in normal position, and C-shaped horns whose form is echoed in the involute tails of the body bands as well as in the jaws; the narrow upper frieze contains the figures of birds confronting each other, two above each half of the T'ao-t'ieh. The shoulder zone is decorated with dragon figures in antithetical order, to the left and right of sculptural animal heads placed in the central axis of the T'ao-t'ieh faces below. Around the neck runs a band where, most anomalously, prostrate dragons appear. On the under side of the flaring mouth there is a wreath of broad lancets filled with lancet-shaped, hooked points. All of these ornaments are executed in flat relief on finely drawn, mainly angular, meander ground. Up to the shoulder, each ornament is bisected by strong vertical flanges; they cut through the middle of the faces and separate the adjoining units. Above the shoulder, flanges are omitted. Noteworthy are the asymmetrical design elements observable in the T'ao-t'ieh faces and bodies. I know of no other instance of eyes mismatched as they are here: oval in the left halves, round in the right halves, on both foot and body of the vessel. As our eyes wander up along the axis, other asymmetries will be caught, for there are many of them. They do not, however, affect the "expression" of this remarkable bronze.

    Published: Young, *Art Styles of Ancient Shang*, No. 52; briefly mentioned in A. Priest, "Chinese Bronzes," The Metropolitan Museum of Art *Bulletin*, N.S. IV, December, 1945, p. 109.

    The earliest type of this class is represented by the *Tsun* from the Sackler Collections, No. 3. The wide gap between it and the Metropolitan Museum piece can be bridged by an outstanding Style II *Tsun* formerly owned by C. T. Loo (Umehara, *Seika*, I, 33; *idem, Kodōki keitai*, pl. 9: 6; Jung Keng, *Shang Chou*, fig. 525); an early Style III vessel in the Palace Museum collection (*Ku Kung*, vol. 35; *Shang Chou*, fig. 498); and a squatter, developed Style III vessel formerly owned by Yamanaka, New York (*Seika*, I, 32; *Kodōki keitai*, pl. 9:5; *Shang Chou*, fig. 497). The Metropolitan Museum piece in turn precedes the Cologne *Tsun*, No. 30.

30 TSUN
Shang, Style IV
H. 16⅝ in., DIAM. (at mouth) 13½ in.
Museum für Ostasiatische Kunst der Stadt Köln

Similar to the preceding type but of a different silhouette, this tall vessel is also built up in three horizontal sections. The foot flares and its base is molded; the body juts out widely over the foot; the trumpet-shaped mouth rises more steeply, then flares more suddenly. In contrast to the preceding type, moreover, the neck is left bare, its ornamentation being limited to two fine "bowstrings." The T'ao-t'ieh on the foot recurs in larger dimension on the belly. Above the larger T'ao-t'ieh runs a narrow frieze whose sections are occupied by *monoculi*. On the shoulder there are dragon figures with turned heads and hooked beaks, interrupted by short flanges and by buffalo heads in low relief, with scale-marked horns; their muzzles overlap the edge of the shoulder. The distribution of the vertical flanges corresponds to what we saw in No. 29. The animal ornaments as well as the ground spirals are cast in very shallow relief. There is a lack of vigor and freshness in the décor of this vessel which curiously contrasts with the monumental power and *noblesse* of its shape. There is a gray-green, thin patina with light incrustations and a few corroded spots.

Published: *Museum Guide* (Cologne), 1927, fig. 26; F. Fischer, *Chinesisches Tagebuch*, 1942, fig. 130; *Meisterwerke im Museum für Ostasiatische Kunst*, 1963, No. 63.

Apparently this magnificent type of vessel was destined to disappear in the course of the Western Chou period, if not even earlier. Its beginnings may take us back into the pre-Anyang period. A fine, glazed, shouldered, pottery *Tsun*, with flaring mouth but, characteristically, no foot ring, was excavated at the Ming-kung-lu site of Cheng-chou, a site contemporaneous with Upper Erh-li-kang, hence possibly still Middle Shang in date; see *Kaogu*, 1965/10, pl. 4:7.

31 FANG CHIA
Shang, Style IV
H. 12⅛ in., w. (at base of body) 6½ in.
Albright-Knox Art Gallery, Buffalo

A tetrapod in the form of a rectangular vessel has strongly curved sides and sturdy, splayed legs which are rhombic in section, Like the round *Chia* types, the vessel has a loop handle attached to one of the broad sides. Strong quadrangular posts, topped by tectiform heads, stand on the rims of the narrow sides. Scored flanges accentuate the ridges and corners of these heads, as well as the corners of the vessel's body. The vessel is covered by a flat lid which, instead of a handle, is provided with two small bird figures in the round, sitting back to back. The surfaces are decorated all over, the only plain areas being the lower parts of the handle and posts, and the inner sides of the legs. The ornaments are done in flat relief on a ground of angular spirals and inlaid with a black paste. On the tapering feet we recognize small, thready, and elongated dragons in antithetically designed half-lancets, as dictated by the given surfaces. On the broad side where the handle sits, arranged in three registers, are first a T'ao-t'ieh, next, whorl medallions, and topmost, two dragons facing toward the corners. Quite different is the décor of the other sides where, surprisingly, the face and body of an owl appear. The eyes and the beak of the owl are rendered sculpturally, the rest in flat relief. In the lower register we discern the wings and short tail of the owl, and intricate, small dragons within the wings. In the upper register, above the eyes whose surrounding disks, oddly, display strong eyebrows, rise pointed ears or horns which apparently must be read as belonging to the owl. Where the handle joins the upper part of the body, at the level of the third register, there sits a simplified T'ao-t'ieh mask with engraved features. The lid is decorated with a border frieze occupied by flat relief birds set face to face. The effect of a decoration consisting simply of very finely drawn squarish spirals can be studied on the roof-shaped pillar heads. There is a one-character inscription. The patina is olive-green with traces of red.

Published: P. J. Kelleher, in *The Buffalo Fine Arts Academy, Gallery Notes*, XVIII, No. 2; Consten, *Das alte China*, pl. 28.

Square variants of originally round types of vessels such as the *Ting*, the *Chia*, the *Hu*, the *Tsun* beaker and the shouldered *Tsun*, came to be favored in late Shang, demonstrating a trend toward architectonic effects—with the concomitant loss of the ceramic affinities characteristic of the early bronze shapes. The *Chia* types in our exhibition, Nos. 4, 8, 14, are too far removed and too early to account for the shape of this late *Chia* with its characteristically S-curved profile, a feature that may have come into being in round *Chia* tripods no earlier than during the phases of Style IV.

A magnificent early Style IV *Chia* in the Freer Gallery (*Freer Gallery Bronzes*, pl. 4) still shows the body divided by a constriction; in two later Style IV specimens (Umehara, *Kodōki keitai*, pl. 28:5, 7) the walls form unbroken curves. In agreement with the rectangular body, the hitherto round pillar tops are transformed into the angular, roof-shaped ones, which recur in the Kansas City specimen, No. 32.

That the owl appears on a vessel of this type seems quite exceptional, while it is commonly found on vessels of the *Yu*, *Chih*, and *Kuang* classes.

32 FANG CHIA
Shang, Style V
H. 13½ in., w. 8½ in.
Nelson-Atkins Gallery, Kansas City, Mo. (Nelson Fund)

This tetrapod is similar in shape to the preceding one, but with flanges added to the legs. With the exception of the thready dragon figures on the legs, the décor is cast in relief. The wide lower register is occupied by T'ao-t'ieh masks with bulging oval eyes, pointed ears, jaws curving out to display teeth and fangs on both sides, and with the involute tips of the horns emphasized by very high relief. The masks on the wide sides of the vessel are flanked by dragons in vertical position. The much narrower band above the masks contains bird figures facing the middle. On the flaring part below the rim are rows of broad lancets filled with triangular geometric figures. Small T'ao-t'ieh masks, facing upward, appear on the roof-shaped tops of the strong posts rising from the rim above the narrow sides. Here, too, flanges are added in the middle of each of these masks, contributing to a heavier and more pronouncedly architectonic appearance of the vessel. The flat lid carries a single bird figure in the round. The bird, perhaps an owl, stands in the middle between the flanking posts. Behind the bird, a strong, loop handle is attached to the wide side of the vessel; it is topped by a massive animal mask, the horns of which cut across the lancets under the rim. In the narrow band beneath the lancets, at either side of the mask, whorl circles take the place of the bird figures on the remaining faces.

Published: *International Exhibition of Chinese Art*, London, 1935–36, No. 232; *Yeh-chung p'ien-yü*, Pt. II, shang:19, 20; Priest, *Chinese Bronzes*, 1938, No. 47; *Pacific Cultures*, Golden Gate International Exhibition, San Francisco, 1939, p. 36, No. 5; Jung Keng, *Shang Chou*, fig. 460; Waterbury, *Early Chinese Symbols and Literature*, pl. 73; M. Feddersen, *Chinesisches Kunstgewerbe*, 1955, p. 124; E. Reischauer and J. Fairbank, *East Asia: The Great Tradition*, 1960, pl. 8; M. Sullivan, *Introduction to Chinese Art*, 1961, pl. 10; Nelson-Atkins Gallery, *Handbook of the Collections*, 4th ed., p. 170.

The two *Fang Chia*, Nos. 31 and 32, present no dramatic, striking contrast. The changes are subtle, but nevertheless unmistakable. Even a detail such as the tectiform cap of the pillars can tell us clearly of the new tendency at work in No. 32. Presumably the two bronzes are not far apart in time, representing, it seems, late IV and early V, respectively.

33 HU
Shang, Style IV–V
H. 16 in., W. 11 in.
Nelson-Atkins Gallery of Art, Kansas City, Mo. (Nelson Fund)

A large, oval vessel, this bronze is of the type described under No. 17, but is distinguished by slightly altered proportions and a decoration of strikingly changed character. The foot is taller, and the silhouette, in addition to its bolder sweep, is accentuated by lateral flanges. Unnecessary from the point of view of function or structure, these flanges are added for effect or expressiveness. They are scored with transverse grooves and interrupted by deep notches at the level of each of the narrow, plain strips which separate the five décor zones. For the proper understanding of the formal qualities of the decoration it is important to observe features other than the various motifs assembled. Such features are: the strictly followed axial order and frontal symmetry; the elimination of motifs such as the "monoculi" and S-spirals that would disrupt this symmetry; the absence of repetition of motifs; and the variation in the technical treatment of the several zones of décor.

The dominating motif, in the tallest zone at the widest part of the vessel, is a T'ao-t'ieh mask with large, round eyes with circular depressions, with C-shaped horns and formidable claws—a mask that coheres as a relief unit set off from the ground of fine, round spirals surrounding it. Its sheer size, corporeality, and quasi-realism contrast strikingly with the restrained, geometric, and unreal appearance of the corresponding design in the *Hu* of the Sackler Collections, No. 17. The friezes at the foot and the neck, lowermost and topmost, are cast in low relief, but the one at the top shows zoomorphs with protuberant eyes. The zone above the big T'ao-t'ieh displays a face consisting of isolated parts which stand out in relief against the fine and dense spiral pattern of the ground. The patterning of the isolated parts with barbed spirals is a trait reminiscent of the preceding Styles III and IV. The frieze atop the last one, at the narrowest part of the vessel, shows two dragons confronting a ram's head, in high relief, that straddles the fourth and fifth zones. Two vertical lugs decorated with T'ao-t'ieh faces in relief, sporting bushy eyebrows, extend from the zone of the dragons down to the middle of the adjoining zone.

A few details remain to be mentioned. On the forehead of the large T'ao-t'ieh an elevated diamond shape appears, flanked by the sunken glyphs for "hand," which are similar to the shape of the mighty claws of this T'ao-t'ieh. Between its eyes and nostrils two small scale signs are placed in inverted position. The contour of the mouth is lined with teeth formed by scalloped curves. Finally, between the little monster figures on the foot rim are inserted small ram's heads, upside down, in flat relief, almost like pictographs.

Published: *ACASA*, IX, 1955, p. 87; Umehara, *Inkyo*, pl. 93; J. D. Chen, *Essays on Chinese Antiquities*, Hong Kong, 1952, p. 149; Consten, *Das alte China*, pl. 19; Nelson-Atkins Gallery *Handbook*, 4th ed., p. 170.

34 KUANG
Shang, Style V
H. 7½ in., L. 8 in., W. 4¾ in.
Norton Gallery and School of Art, West Palm Beach

This ewer is shaped like a sauce-boat, whose asymmetrical rim and ascending spout is covered with a lid suggesting the body of a monstrous animal. Above an oval, hollow ring foot, with a small open arch in the middle of each long side, the vessel bulges moderately, then flares in varying degrees toward the asymmetrical rim and spout. At the low end, opposite the spout, a loop handle is attached to the body. The décor, executed in relief on a ground of rounded spirals, is far more complex in motifs and arrangement than in any of the symmetrically shaped vessels. If the long sides were seen side by side, however, the overall design of each would exactly mirror the other. On the foot, to the right of the small arch, we note the figure of an elephant with raised trunk; to the left of the arch, that of a short-bodied dragon juxtaposed to a mighty claw. This claw issues from a leg that cuts across the middle frieze and the foot ring, and the leg in turn belongs to a sinuous, slender, band-like "body" that springs from the big animal head above the spout. A corresponding foreleg, similarly loosely placed along the serpentine "body," shares the space under the spout with a dragon figure next to the rim. To the right of the serpentine, band body with its large, convolute tail, another dragon is squeezed into the space limited by a vertical flange in the middle of the upper frieze. To the right of this flange, which continues downward as far as the foot, there are two larger dragons of varied postures in the middle zone, and one comfortably reclining S-shaped figure in the upper zone adjoining the rim.

On the lid, a kind of spine is formed by a crest with neatly incised, barbed spirals, which extends from the apex of the big monster head to the upright ears of an animal head in flat relief at the opposite end. While the big monster head and its bottle-shaped horns are sculpted in the round, its features are engraved in the plain surfaces. Its eyes are like those of a T'ao-t'ieh, but the mouth, with ferociously bared teeth, is more like a beast's. Under its horns issue the serpentine bands, described above, that seem to represent the beast's body as seen from either side. Along the spine, and adjoining the upright ears of the mask, there are two tiger figures, followed by small creatures whose bodies are marked with lozenges; neither of these is visible in our reproduction. The flat mask at the end is of unusual and surprising design. Its large, round T'ao-t'ieh eyes, set in hooked lid outlines, are surrounded by a plain surface with large spirals deeply and precisely engraved below and around the eyes; between the eyes is a broad band of small scales which bifurcates to form eyebrows above the eyes. Possibly this scaly formation has to be read as the bodies of two serpentine creatures, whose heads take the place of the muzzle of the mask's face. A short, angular "tongue" marked with water zigzag lines projects from the mask; it may have served to lift the lid in the proper manner.

The handle, too, is given a zoomorphic shape, again of a rather uncommon character. The head is plain; the eyes are rendered as round elevations within a concentric circle but without lids; the ears are plain and hollow, like spoons; and there is no distinct indication of a mouth. What should correspond to the forelegs look like arms in reversed position; large clawed feet springing from the base of the handle and reaching down into the foot zone seem to be the feet of the monster on the handle. Under the handle, clinging to it as though with an effort, there is an appendage in the form of a small quadruped very like a small bear.

Published: Umehara, *Inkyo*, pl. 110, with top view of the lid.

For reasons not hitherto understood, some of the *Kuang* vessels were decorated with exceedingly diversified and intricate zoomorphic designs, while others were unadorned. The history and origin of the *Kuang* are obscure. The type seems to have appeared only in late Shang and to have disappeared some time in Western Chou. The latest example known, to date, is a provincial piece of awkward proportions found with an important group of early Western Chou bronzes at Yen-tun-shan in Tan-t'u, Kiangsu, in 1954 (*Wen-wu*, 1955/5; T. Higuchi, in *Tōyōshi Kenkyū*, XVI/3, 1957, 258ff.; Watson, *Archaeology in China*, pl. 65; *idem, Ancient Chinese Bronzes*, pl. 50a). In contrast to the older types it stands on four short feet, like the *I* or *Yih* ewers which replaced the *Kuang* by late Western Chou.

The Norton Gallery specimen forms a link between two distinct types: (1) vessels without flanges and horizontal divisions, where the motif of a serpentine body sweeps down from the lid, and (2) those decorated in compartments.

(cont.)

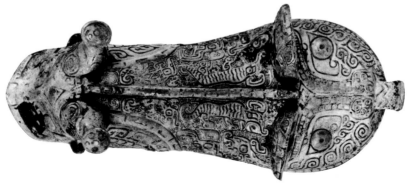

No. 34: lid from above.

Another *Kuang* combining the compartmental decoration with the overlapping sinuous body with clawed feet, and thus resembling the Norton specimen, was published by Waterbury, *Early Chinese Symbols and Literature*, pl. 7 (also Karlgren, "Notes on the Grammar of Early Bronze Décor," pl. 1c). Type (1) is represented in the Sumitomo collection (Umehara, *Senoku seishō*, New Acquisitions, 1961, No. 241, pl. 1), in the Fogg Art Museum (Mizuno, *Bronzes and Jades*, pl. 54), and in Huang Chün's *Tsun-ku-chai*, Pt. I, 3:19). Type (2) is represented in the Hakuzuru Museum (Umehara, *Kanan Anyō ihō*, pl. 43; also Mizuno, *Bronzes and Jades*, pl. 55: the lid topped by an elephant head) and, again, in the Sumitomo collection (*Senoku seishō*, rev. ed., 1934, No. 114). One motif in our No. 34, the small elephant figure, recurs in the last-mentioned Sumitomo piece, No. 114. There the elephant is followed by a hare; on a Freer Gallery *Kuang* he is faced by the hare (*Freer Gallery Bronzes*, pl. 7). The hare makes his appearance again—a little less distinctly rendered, with shorter ears and as if clad in a tiger's skin—in the Hakuzuru piece with the elephant head on the lid. These realistic animal motifs, to which the small bear under the handle of the Norton piece must be added, tie the latter more definitely to type (2). Moreover, the Norton vessel, that in Waterbury's book, and the Sumitomo piece (No. 114) all have monster heads displaying bottle-horns, which the type (1) vessels do not possess. The bottle-horns, while not *de rigueur*, are very common in *Kuang* which are typologically later than any of the vessels mentioned above. Such later *Kuang* are the figs. 675–679, 681, 682, 685 in Jung Keng's *Shang Chou*. Only the last number, a *Kuang* from the Oscar Raphael collection now in the Fitzwilliam Museum, is later than Shang in Jung Keng's estimate. The features which permit us to determine the later date of the vessels noted from Jung Keng's corpus are mainly these: flare and molding of the foot; flanges with spurs; rectangularity of the body (682); and, of course, the character of the décor.

In sum, the following chronological sequence is suggested:

1. Tsun-ku-chai *Kuang*,
2. Sumitomo collection, No. 241,
3. Fogg Art Museum *Kuang* from the Winthrop collection,
4. the vessel illustrated in Florance Waterbury's book,
5. Norton Gallery specimen, our No. 34,
6. Hakuzuru Museum piece,
7. Sumitomo collection, No. 114.

As a corollary to this sequence we are enabled to see clearly that the sinuous bands in the fourth and fifth examples are derived from the more powerful and precise design of the Tiger bodies in the first three examples.

35 YÜ
Shang, Style V
H. 6 9/16 in., DIAM. 9 9/16 in.
Museum für Kunst und Gewerbe, Hamburg

A round bowl that widens evenly toward its slightly flaring rim is supported by a similarly flaring, but much narrower, ring-foot. The décor consists of zoomorphic ornaments arranged in three zones, cast in relief on a ground of squarish spirals. Plain strips separate the zones horizontally; straight, scored flanges mark the vertical sections. The tallest zone, in the middle, is filled by three bodied T'ao-t'ieh flanked by small dragons in headlong position. The protuberant eyes of these T'ao-t'ieh are shaped as ovals or, rather, rounded rectangles, with horizontal slits; they have no lids. Their mouths show small teeth along the inner contours; their jaws are rolled inward. "Dragons" with hooked beaks, and mushroom horns on their turned heads, are placed in the compartments of the foot zone, in antithetical pairs. In the frieze under the rim we find other "dragons" with the same kind of horns but strange, elongated upper jaws or trunks marked by tiny scales; they face toward a small animal head with ram's horns, in full relief. The patina, according to Jakobsen's description, is gray-green and smooth, showing spots of dark green and reddish brown and some malachite incrustations.

Published: Jean-Pierre Dubosc, *Mostra d'Arte Cinese*, Venice, 1954, No. 25, pl. 4 below; Consten, *Das alte China*, pl. 26 below; Dexel, *Chinesische Bronzen*, p. 23; K. Jakobsen, "Chinesische Bronzen," 107–110, fig. 3; Mizuno, *Bronzes and Jades*, pl. 29.

This type of vessel which is less common than, and distinguishable from, the *Kuei*, has often been grouped with the latter class. In Jung Keng's comprehensive *Shang Chou*, for instance, vessels of the same shape and without handles are called *Kuei* (figs. 233, 235, 236, 238, 241), while two pieces are listed at the very end as *Yü* (figs. 989, 990). But his No. 990, with upturned loop handles, again has analogues among the *Kuei* (figs. 284–286). Describing the type in question in his *Ancient Chinese Bronzes*, p. 29, Watson rightly insists on using the term *Yü* for it, "as inscribed on a piece excavated at Hsi Pei Kang, and on the bowl . . . of the Marquis of Yen" (cf. *KKHP*, VII, 1954, p. 25 and pl. 9, for the Hsi-pei-kang bronze; *Wen-wu*, 1955/8, 16–27; T. Higuchi, "A New Study," p. 23, pl. 6:1; W. Watson, *Archaeology in China*, pl. 61; idem, *Ancient Chinese Bronzes*, pl. 43a, for the bronze from the Yen State, which belongs with the hoard from Hai-tao Ying-tzu in Ling-yüan, Liao-ning. On the authority of these inscriptions the term *Yü* is an authentic name for this type of vessel, and its use for the purpose of distinguishing this type from the common *Kuei* is fully justified.

Jakobsen's perfectly acceptable "late Shang" date is based to some extent on a comparison of the Hamburg *Yü* with a similar specimen in the Pillsbury collection, which fortunately can be studied in this exhibition (No. 36). There can be no doubt whatsoever about the relationship of the two vessels: the Hamburg *Yü* is earlier than the Minneapolis *Yü*, typologically as well as stylistically, as pointed out under No. 36.

36   YÜ
Shang, Style V
H. 7 in., DIAM. 9⅞ in.
The Minneapolis Institute of Arts; bequest of Alfred F. Pillsbury

This round vessel without handles is similar to the preceding type, but with gently curved rather than straight sides, and more sophisticated in design. The foot is raised by a vertical base which, receding slightly, gives prominence to the flaring ledge of the foot. The molding of the mouth rim, too, transforms an uneventful, not to say inexpressive part (as in No. 23) into a significant, highly articulate form. Something comparable has happened to the flanges. In exactly the same positions as in No. 35, they here assume—through weightier dimensions, through the salient tips of the short sections at the top and at the bottom, and especially through the sharp spurs at the top of the main sections—an expressive function.

To evaluate the subtle, almost elusive differences in the treatment of the décor of the two vessels we are comparing is far more difficult. These differences do not amount to differences of style, but only of design, so that at best they may reveal a "tendency." The meaning of a tendency such as we believe to be discernible cannot be judged from the narrow context of the two vessels alone but requires a clear concept of the stylistic changes at large.

The relief of the figures in the Pillsbury *Yü* appears to be slightly more pronounced than in the Hamburg *Yü*, most noticeably in the large, C-shaped horns with their troughed surfaces. The fact of their relative largeness and relative plainness deserves to be noted, as does the fact that the fangs are large and plain. The sunken lineament on the T'ao-t'ieh body is unlike that of the corresponding part in No. 35—less regular, less accountable than the sequence of spirals there. The strange dragons with scaly trunks in the upper zone of No. 35 are here replaced by typical late Shang motifs. The *lei-wen* spirals of the ground are a trifle less carefully executed; the barbs in particular, conscientiously observed in the other piece, are largely omitted here. The eyes of the T'ao-t'ieh, finally, are round, large, alert in expression, greatly contrasting with the sleepy, oval eyes of the other T'ao-t'ieh. Taken in their entirety, these traits would seem to support the later date postulated on typological grounds; they are farther removed from older Shang styles than is the Hamburg specimen. There is a smooth, gray-green patina.

The vessel bears an inscription in which each sign is decipherable, but the inscription remains unintelligible as a whole. The meanings of the several characters are given in Karlgren's *Catalogue* under No. 37. It is peculiar that of the cyclical characters used in Shang names there occur *kuei, i* (twice), and possibly also *ting*.

Published: Karlgren, *Chinese Bronzes in the Pillsbury Collection*, No. 37, p. 106, pl. 54.

37   FANG I
Shang, Style V
H. 10 in., W. 5½ in., D. (at bottom of lid) 4½ in.
Mr. and Mrs. Frederick M. Mayer, New York City

A rectangular box has slightly spreading sides and a tectiform lid, which is surmounted by a knob echoing the shape of the lid. Straight, densely scored flanges accentuate the corners and central axes of both the body and the lid. These flanges are interrupted only under the knob at the ridge of the lid. In the middle of each of the four sides of the foot are small, open arches, half the height of the foot. The décor is designed and cast with astonishing precision and clarity. Dragons with hooked beaks and tufts are placed antithetically in the compartments above the T'ao-t'ieh mask, and dragons with small bottle horns below. The mask consists of disconnected parts marked with beautifully executed, rounded and barbed spirals on a ground of square spirals. A mask of analogous design but facing upward appears on the lid. Like the dragon figures, the parts of the masks are raised in relief: the oval, lidless eyes, the eyebrows and clawed feet, and—always in variations of the same form—large involute horns, ears, and mouths. The straight, hooked, forehead shield in the middle is also in raised relief. The patina is a smooth, light green.

Not previously published.

I know of no other *Fang I* to match this exquisite specimen in proportions, design, and refined technique. A comparable vessel, with regard to the unbroken flanges and the form of the T'ao-t'ieh, is in the Hakuzuru Museum (*Hakkaku*, 20; Jung Keng, *Shang Chou*, fig. 595; Umehara, *Nihon Seika*, IV, 278). Two others, with partly interrupted flanges and T'ao-t'ieh masks constructed of disengaged parts, are in the collections of Dr. Wessén (Karlgren, "Wessén Collection," pls. 1–3) and of the late N. Hiroumi of Kobe (*Nihon Seika*, IV, 279). Among further examples listed by Karlgren, none is more important than a find from Hou-chia-chuang, Anyang (Li Chi, *The Beginnings*, pl. 6), which secures the Shang date of this type.

Compared with the slightly larger, splendid *Fang I* from Cincinnati, No. 38, the Mayer specimen reveals affinities with older styles, affinities which in the terser and more compact statement of the Cincinnati piece are no longer traceable. The retention of large spirals within the zoomorphic elements as a significant part of the design is a case in point; the retention of the spiral-filled, hooked shield in the middle

is another. The Mayer specimen stands much closer to the rare and important Style III *Fang I* in *Yeh-chung p'ien-yü*, III, 22 (also Loehr, "Bronze Styles," fig. 12) than does No. 38. The form of the flanges alone offers a criterion for the earlier date of No. 37.

While grouped under Style V on account of the relief technique used in combination with the fine, even, and neutral meander ground, the décor of this *Fang I* actually represents a distinct variety, Style V (a), the nature and chronological position of which was tentatively and briefly described in my article on "Bronze Styles," p. 48. I am mentioning this here because among the bronzes assembled in our exhibition the present specimen is the only one to demonstrate distinctly the characteristics of Style V (a).

It is common practice to use the phrase "dissolved T'ao-t'ieh" to describe the fact of its features being disconnected, or rendered in separated parts. Actually, suggesting as it does a process of dissolution or deformation, the phrase does not apply in this case. The dissolution of the T'ao-t'ieh motif took place only in Western Chou (see Nos. 53, 56, 57).

38   FANG I
Shang, Style V
H. 11½ in., W. 7⅜ in., D. 6¼ in.
Cincinnati Art Museum; gift of the family of Mr. and Mrs. Charles F. Williams

This rectangular casket, with a roof-shaped lid and knob, is fortified by heavy, scored, straight flanges at the corners and in the middle of each face of both vessel and lid. The flanges are interrupted in accordance with the plain strips separating the decorated zones. The sides widen somewhat toward the upper edge of the casket. In the middle of each side of the foot, which is hollow, there is a small open arch, a feature that was to disappear in Western Chou. The décor is cast in relief on a ground pattern of rounded spirals designed with astonishing precision. T'ao-t'ieh masks in coherent bodies, with round eyes and circular pupils, C-shaped horns, and involute mouth contours with teeth, dominate the widest zone of décor on the vessel and, facing upward, fill the surfaces of the tectiform lid. In the fields above the T'ao-t'ieh masks, we find dragons confronting one another, and in the fields below the masks, a different kind of dragon turned away from each other. Miniature masks in low relief appear on the knob.

In the vessel as well as in the lid there is a cast, sunken glyph whose meaning is not safely established as yet, even though it is known from several instances of vessels or tools. This glyph is a combination of a cross-shaped sign, usually called *ya-hsing*, "shape of the character *ya*," and the pictograph of a man seen frontally while his head is turned to the side as if he were in a state of uncertainty or doubt; in fact this pictograph resembles, and has often been read as, the character *i*, meaning "doubt," or the character *ni*, "imitate," that has the classifier "hand" added. Takada, in his *Ku Chou P'ien* (ch. 8 : 23 b), takes the cross shape to represent diagrammatically the Grand Hall of the ancestral temple, an explanation given also by Sun Hai-po (*Chung-kuo wen-tzu-hsüeh*, Tokyo, 1941, 59 a) who even uses the exalted term, Ming T'ang, "Bright Hall." The combination of the temple symbol with the figure underneath might express, therefore, an idea such as "following the way of the ancestors." But this interpretation is not generally accepted. Jung Keng, for one, while assembling a fair number of examples of the glyph, refrains from giving a reading (*Chin Wen Pien*, 1959, p. 822). A particularly fine specimen of this glyph found on a bronze chisel formerly in the collection of C. T. Loo, New York, and reproduced from a rubbing in the Japanese encyclopedia on palaeography and calligraphy, *Shodō Zenshū* (Vol. I, 1954, pl. 24, text p. 170), is presented, likewise, without any explanation in S. Umehara's pertinent entry. Since this glyph seems to occur mainly by itself, it may, of course, stand as a name or clan sign rather than a word or phrase.

Published: *Cincinnati Art Museum News*, II/8, December 1947; Loehr, "Bronze Styles," fig. 18; White, *Bronze Culture*, p. 52.

This vessel is a classic example of its class as well as of its style. It stands midway between the older form of No. 37 and the later form of No. 56. Compared with the former, it has lost something of an antique richness and stiff grace but has gained in sophisticated articulation (flanges; recessed foot). Measured by the excess of the Metropolitan Museum piece, No. 56, the Cincinnati vessel delights by its vigor and restraint.

39   LI-TING
Shang, Style V
H. 7½ in., w. 5¾ in.
The Metropolitan Museum of Art, New York City; gift of Mrs. John Marriott, Mrs. John Barry Ryan, Gilbert W. Kahn, Roger Wolfe Kahn, 1949

This tripod has plain, cylindrical legs, which taper slightly toward the bottom. The bowl has the shape described under Nos. 21 and 26, but its proportions are altered to create the effect of greater heaviness. The ears on the rim, in particular, being thicker at the top than at the base, contribute much toward this effect. So do the three T'ao-t'ieh masks above the legs, which are rendered as compact relief bodies with extraordinarily strong median flanges. The inner lineament, compared to the intricate detail in the Victoria & Albert specimen, No. 26, is radically simplified. In the meander ground there is more diversity than in earlier vessels; the spirals are rather irregular, and long striae are used beside them. The ornament in the neck belt, which consists of rows of spirals slanting to the left and to the right from the middle of each section, is of great simplicity. The middle is marked by a small, hooked shield with a ridge above the contractions of the body. The surface is covered by an even, light green patina.

Not previously published.

A comparably vigorous design, but with a frieze of undulating dragons instead of the unassuming band of spirals, and with legs decorated with incised hanging lancets, may be seen in a *Li-Ting* of the Freer Gallery of Art (No. 47.11).

40 YU
Shang, Style V
H. 10¼ in., w. 6¾ in.
The Minneapolis Institute of Arts; bequest of Alfred F. Pillsbury

The silhouette of this profusely decorated, oval container, with lid and handle, is intensified by spiky flanges. Swelling strongly above the foot, the body then moves upward in a gently concave outline that continues into the collar of the lid. A sharp cornice separates the collar from the domed top of the lid, which is surmounted by a conical knob. On both sides of the lid, level with the cornice, large upturned hooks jut out with dramatic effect. The handle, which swings over the long axis, is attached to knobs at the centers of the wide sides, at the level of the uppermost zone of the body. The décor is cast in relief on angular meanders. Long-bodied creatures with birds' heads occupy the quadrants of the foot rim. In the widest and tallest zone, above the foot, there are large, addorsed birds in each of the quadrants. This zone is separated from that below the rim, which is occupied by four dragons, by a band of vertical ribs. On the collar of the lid there are four birds, confronted like the dragons below them. On the dome of the lid, a circle of ribs again appears, surrounded by a narrow band with elongated birds similar to those on the foot rim. Large, sunken cicada figures appear at the under sides of the projecting hooks. Small cicadas in headlong position adorn the knob. On the handle are four elongated dragon figures with plain bodies, heading upward, while the ends of the handle are masked by animal heads with mushroom-shaped horns in the round. The patina, as described by Karlgren, is gray-green with patches of sharp green.

The inscription consists of three (?) glyphs in vertical order, framed by a *ya-hsing*, that is, a rectangle with recessed corners, hence cross-shaped, a common symbol, of uncertain significance, which Karlgren takes to mean an "ancestral-temple piece."

Published: Karlgren, *Pillsbury Collection*, No. 16, p. 50, pls. 22, 23.

A very similar *Yu* is in the Worcester Art Museum (P. Ackerman, *Ritual Bronzes*, pl. 8; P. B. Cott, *Art Through Fifty Centuries*, Worcester Art Museum, 1948, fig. 25), which, agreeing in all essentials, must be strictly contemporaneous with the Pillsbury piece; possibly the two came from the same caster's shop.

The relative position of these magnificent vessels can be determined quite exactly within the typological series of which they form part. It is a series of *Yu* vessels with lateral hooks projecting from the lid and with flanges whose increasingly flamboyant and complicated form reveals a definite progression, a series which consists of vessels decorated in Style V exclusively:

1. Formerly Holmes collection; J. Trübner, *Yu und Kuang*, pl. 14. *Yu* with low-collared lid, straight, low flanges, small hooks which are not upturned.

2. Cernuschi Museum; *ibid.*, pl. 15. Low-collared lid, straight low flanges, small hooks which are drawn upward to some extent.

3. Cull collection; Yetts, *The Cull Chinese Bronzes*, No. 3. Similar to the preceding piece as far as the criteria in question are concerned.

4. Sumitomo collection; *Yu und Kuang*, pl. 13; *Senoku Seishō*, rev. ed., 1934, pl. 20, No. 75. The collar of the lid is higher; the flanges are low, and on the lid, straight; but for the first time we observe a small spur in the vertical flanges flanking the big T'ao-t'ieh; the lateral hooks are sharply drawn upward.

5. Pillsbury collection, our No. 40. For the first time, the collar of the lid is higher than the neck-belt; the flanges, also for the first time, have strong spurs both on the lid and on the body, the latter projecting at the tops of each of the three décor zones. The hooks are large; their tips reach above the ends of the flanges of the lid. Instead of the T'ao-t'ieh, ubiquitous in the preceding items, birds and a band of vertical ribs appear on the belly and on the dome of the lid.

6. Worcester Art Museum *Yu*, mentioned above. Identical with the preceding specimen as far as the criteria in question are concerned.

7 and 8. Metropolitan Museum, *Yu* vessels from Pao-chi-hsien, Shensi; Trübner, *Yu und Kuang*, pls. 3 and 6; Jung Keng, *Shang Chou*, figs. 607, 608. The proportions have changed further, as the flanges now are wider than ever and the lid now has a much higher dome, while the spurs are made weighty by a somewhat increased width. The lateral hooks, too, are slightly wider than before. In the decoration, the conspicuous belt of vertical ribs remains, but instead of the mixed company of birds and dragons in the other zones there are now birds only.

9 and 10. Freer Gallery and Boston Museum of Fine Arts, a larger and a smaller *Yu* deriving from a second set of bronzes discovered also in Pao-chi-hsien; see Umehara, *Seika*, I, 71, for the larger vessel of the Freer Gallery, and our No. 41 for the smaller vessel in Boston, which is of identical design. Basically, the shapes and the decoration are like those of the preceding two pieces, but there are utterly strange additions and changes. Quadrangular beams are added, with upcurved ends projecting diagonally from the belt of vertical ribs—beams with clumsy, angular, oblique appendages and with molded buffalo heads at their upturned under sides. The lateral hooks of the lid, too, are transformed into buffalo heads. The ends of the handles are masked by animal heads with five-pronged antlers like those on the preceding two vessels, but the handles are troughed and provided with sculptured buffalo heads.

In this series, the Boston *Yu*, No. 41, and its companion

piece in Washington represent the latest formulation, the *ne plus ultra* in a meaningful progression of designs which increasingly stress expressive form. The shape of the vessel as such remains unchanged. The metamorphoses we are able to observe have no bearing on the function of these vessels, but only on their appearance. At any rate, the relative date of the *Yu* from Minneapolis is incontrovertibly clear: it is earlier than the Pao-chi *Yu* of the Metropolitan Museum, preceding the latter by one step, as it were.

The question of the nature of the two Pao-chi hoards and of the likely date of the *Yu* vessels will be taken up under No. 41 below. Here I should like to emphasize the significance of the typological sequence of the *Yu* listed above: in its coherence and logicality, that sequence suggests artistic thought and realizations in an uninterrupted tradition. Consequently the Pao-chi *Yu* of the Metropolitan Museum cannot easily be removed from its antecedents, which tie it to Shang traditions. As for the Boston and Freer *Yu*, we have to admit that the innovations they display are devolutionary rather than evolutionary in character; there is a destructive touch in their sculptural abandon. They do not actually continue the series but close it. It is not inconceivable that they were early Chou products.

Two relevant features should be mentioned in this connection. None of the Pao-chi *Yu* have openwork flanges such as are widely seen in Western Chou bronzes. Second, the element of the vertical ribs, while conspicuous in early Western Chou décor—e.g., the *K'ang Hou Kuei* of the Malcolm collection—appears to go back to Shang, as attested by a magnificent marble *Kuei* in the Moriya collection (Umehara, *Selected Treasures*, pl. 63). Both of these features would favor a Shang date for the Pao-chi *Yu*.

41   YU
Late Shang, Style V
H. 14⅛ in., W. 9 in.
Museum of Fine Arts, Boston; Anna Mitchell Richards Fund

This oval container has a high, domed lid with lateral projections, profusely decorated and provided with spurred flanges, similar to the *Yu* of the Pillsbury collection, No. 40, but with novel additions: beams, rectangular in section, that are curved upward at the ends, jut out at right angles from the middle of the four quadrants of the wall. Not wishing to repeat the descriptions given in the entry for No. 40 and the notes relating to the Boston Museum and Freer Gallery vessels appended (under 9 and 10) to that entry, I will merely point out such features as distinguish this remarkable vessel from the Pillsbury *Yu*, which is of slightly earlier design. The flanges are higher here and, instead of the simple, straight scores, show incised patterns of a certain complexity. Their more extravagant design can be seen very clearly in an inconspicuous portion such as that on the foot rim. If the flanges are not incompatible with the structure of the vessel but rather emphasize it, strikingly and expressively, the beams, on the contrary, sallying forth abruptly and with ferocious aggressiveness, are wholly unrelated to the vessel's structure. These beams, with their seemingly unmotivated and undeniably clumsy appendages, rather tend to obscure the form of the vessel. In fact we are here faced for the first time with a design of inorganic and willful character. Another change to note is the troughed shape of the handle and the appearance of the animal heads masking the ends of the handle. The five-pronged antlers with "eyes" surmounting these heads are exactly like those of the Pao-chi-hsien *Yu* in the Metropolitan Museum (see No. 40, commentary, under 7 and 8). But the sculptural buffalo heads attached to the handles have no precedent; again we receive the impression of there being an awkwardly inorganic, willful and, contrived feature. Yet another important change is the transformation of the lateral hooks at the lid into relief masks of water-buffaloes, larger than those on the upturned ends of the beams. As for the ornamentation of the vessel's body, it will be noted that here only birds, and no dragons, appear. Unchanged is the band of vertical ribs. The big birds in the lower zone have crests resembling the "antlers" of the animal heads on the handle. What remains to be mentioned is the refinement and great precision of the design, especially that of the ground spirals, a precision not quite matched by the Pillsbury *Yu*. This high level of workmanship and technique is an interesting trait in view of the circumstance that this vessel formed part, according to Umehara, of a set found at Pao-chi-hsien, Shensi Province, in ancient Western Chou territory. There is a silvery gray patina, with incrustations of green oxide.

Published: Umehara, "The Second Set," pl. 4:1; W. Young, ed., *Application of Science in the Examination of Works of Art*, Museum of Fine Arts, Boston, 1968, color plate.

The provenance of the group to which this *Yu* belongs naturally argues for the possibility that the vessel was manufactured in Chou territory. But it is equally possible that it was brought thither from Shang territory or, for that matter, from the Shang capital. Three reasons speak against a Chou origin: (1) the intimate typological connection of the *Yu* with Shang types, as pointed out under No. 40 above; (2) the high technical quality of the casting and designing; and (3) the stylistic diversity of the bronzes from this hoard, enabling us to separate those which resemble Shang bronzes from others which do not. That a vessel such as the Princeton *Kuang*, No. 50, for instance, was produced in the same foundry as the Boston *Yu* seems very unlikely. Compared with the *Kuang*, the *Yu* seems almost like an unadulterated Shang product. We must assume therefore that the "second set from Pao-chi" comprised, like the first, vessels of different origin and, perhaps, date. But the date of the hoard as a whole is irrelevant to what must be our first concern, namely, to understand the relative position of each particular type. The absolute date of individual vessels is of secondary interest as long as we are still struggling with the concept of a total stylistic sequence, even though an ascertainable absolute date does help us in establishing that sequence.

What, for the present, can be said without reservations is that the *Yu* vessels of the "second set" follow soon after those of the "first set"; if the latter can be shown to date from Western Chou rather than Shang, the former would assuredly fall to Western Chou also. Jung Keng, however, maintains a Shang date for the *Yu* of both sets (*Shang Chou*, figs. 607, 608, 612, text p. 413f.; *idem, Yin Chou*, 1958, figs. 174, 175, text p. 54). In a brief reference to the *Yu* of the first set, made apropos of a square *I* inscribed with the same character *ting* as found on those *Yu*, in the recently published catalogue, *Shanghai Museum Bronzes*, under No. 14, Appendix p. 12, they are assigned to the beginning of Chou. Watson, *Ancient Chinese Bronzes*, p. 50, advocates a Chou date for the *Yu* of the first set, but exaggerates when describing them as "a far cry from . . . Shang vessels"; he rightly links the bovine masks of the *Yu* from the "second set" to the buffalo masks on the four handles of a *Kuei* in the Freer Gallery which appears to be of early Western Chou manufacture (*Freer Gallery Bronzes*, 1946, pl. 28). The rare detail of the sculptured buffalo heads on the arc of the handle recurs in a variant form on a *Yu* with an archaizing T'ao-t'ieh décor and hooked flanges in the Palace Museum (*Ku Kung*, Vol. 32), the Western Chou date of which seems unquestionable, although Jung Keng inclined toward Shang (*Shang Chou*, I, p. 414; fig. 613). In his careful description of the first set published in 1933, *Henkin*, Umehara did not definitely commit himself as to a date, though mentioning the fact that the Chinese scholars favored a Shang date, but, rather, underlined the heterogeneous aspect of the find. My own feeling is that the *Yu* from the "second set" may have been cast in a Shang foundry, whose master was not responsible for the awkward additions that seem foreign to the tradition of Shang down to the *Yu* of the first set.

42   LEI
Late Shang or Early Chou
H. 17⅝ in., DIAM. 13¹⁄₁₆ in.
The Metropolitan Museum of Art, New York City; gift of D. Herbert Beskind, 1959

The tall ovoid vessel, of impressive size and noble shape, has a convex shoulder, contracted neck, moderately flaring mouth, and flat lip. It is supported by a low, plain foot-ring and is fitted with three loop handles, two at the shoulder and a smaller one near the bottom, all masked with small, modeled buffalo heads. The shoulder is set off from the body by a broad groove below and by a dip above, where the neck, which is marked by two fine "bowstrings," begins. The decoration is austere, in keeping with the rest; it consists of six large, relief medallions with incised whorls, placed in the shoulder zone. The smooth, dark, olive-green surface with blackish crusts has preserved its metallic character.

Not previously published.

Apparently this vessel represents a well standardized type. There exist virtually identical *Lei*, e.g., one in the Port Arthur Museum (S. Gōto and Y. Sugimura, *Ryojun Hakubutsukan zuroku*, 1943, pl. 15:5), ascribed to the Chou period presumably on the basis of an inscription, and, in the Royal Ontario Museum in Toronto (White, *Bronze Culture*, p. 84, pl. 38), a vessel found near Anyang and likely to be of Shang date. Another example, in the Sumitomo collection, Kyoto, is provided with a lid and rings, suspended from the handles at the shoulder (*Senoku Seishō*, rev. ed., 1934, No. 57, pl. 14).

Not all of the *Lei* were plain. An ornate specimen probably of late Shang date is in the same collection (*ibid.*, No. 56, pl. 13), but its splayed foot separates it typologically from the plain types just mentioned. An important Anyang find is a damaged bronze *Lei* decorated in Style IV, of a slightly different silhouette and with flat bottom, from a tomb in Hsiao-t'un, M238 (see Li Chi, "Studies of Hsiao-t'un Bronzes," Pt. I, in *KKHP*, III, 1948, fig. 17b, pl. 1:2), which secures the late Shang date of the *Lei* type as such. Li Chi compares his bronze with a pottery *Lei* from the same site which also has no foot (*ibid.*, fig. 17a). The outline and the low neck of the pottery piece calls to mind a more famous Shang ceramic piece: the exquisite White Pottery *Lei* of the Freer Gallery (e.g., Umehara, *Inkyo*, pl. 56) with its geometric décor of plain and meander zigzags, a pattern which, in unsurpassed refinement, embellishes the bronze *Li-Ting* of the Brundage collection, No. 21. Gustav Ecke referred to the Freer Gallery *Lei* apropos of a bronze, flat-bottomed, plain *Lei* with low neck in the H. J. v. Lochow collection (G. Ecke, *Sammlung Lochow*, No. 16), which can with confidence be taken to represent an archaic version of this class of vessel.

The Beskind bronze of the Metropolitan Museum is unlikely to be older than Shang V, but the type persisted into Western Chou. Among a group of bronzes excavated in 1954 at P'u-tu-ts'un in Shensi, datable, on account of an inscribed *Ho* of king Mu Wang's lifetime, to about mid-Western Chou, was a *Lei*, decorated and provided with rings and splayed foot, which may be among the latest vessels of this type known. The Sumitomo pieces seem to stand about midway between the *Lei* No. 42 and the P'u-tu-ts'un vessel.

43 FANG LEI
Early Western Chou
H. 24¹¹⁄₁₆ in., W. 14½ in., D. 10⁷⁄₁₆ in.
City Art Museum of Saint Louis

This monumental, square vessel with rounded shoulder and straight neck, on a pyramidal foot with molded base, is covered with a roof-shaped lid. As in the case of the round *Lei*, No. 42, two handles carrying rings are attached to the shoulders, while a third sits low on the body. They are surmounted by animal heads with five-pronged "antlers" shaped like hands with an eye in the middle, similar to the "antlers" of the *Yu*, No. 41. From the ridge of the lid, down the four corners and the middle of each side, run heavy flanges, set with hooks and spikes at varying intervals. The surfaces thus compartmented are filled with symmetrically arranged, zoomorphous designs cast in relief on a ground pattern of squared meanders. At the foot and at the neck of the vessel dragons with beaks, plumes, and curled up tails appear. Most unusual is the décor of the body, where we notice two superposed T'ao-t'ieh masks within one and the same continuous area. Their horns, divided into a rounded part in high relief and a flat, angular part adjoining, are reminiscent of those in the *Yu* from Honolulu, No. 27, which is an earlier vessel. Above the two T'ao-t'ieh are dragons with eyes placed in the center. Dragons or half-T'ao-t'ieh flank high relief masks or handles, respectively, on the shoulders. On the surfaces of the lid are the same T'ao-t'ieh faces as on the body, but smaller and inverted. The patina is of a rich green, according to Kidder's description, with areas of orange-colored cuprite. A cast pictograph in the neck recurs identically in the lid. It was read as "rain" by Menzies, and it does indeed resemble the ancient character for rain which, however, does not seem to be recorded in exactly this form. Kidder takes it to represent "water flowing between two banks," an interpretation compatible with some of the oracle script forms listed by Takada under *tu*, "ditch, drain, river" (Mathews, 6518) in his *Ku Chou P'ien*, ch. 3:21.

Published: Kidder, *Early Chinese Bronzes*, p. 68, pl. 18, whose long bibliographic list is to be enlarged by: Umehara, *Kodōki keitai*, pl. 12:5; Jung Keng, *Shang Chou*, fig. 785.

Jung Keng ascribed this towering, architectonic vessel to the Shang period (*op. cit.*, I, p. 449). The inscription does not contradict this date which was also upheld by Menzies (*An Exhibition of Ancient Chinese Ritual Bronzes*, The Detroit Institute of Arts, 1940, No. 20). The design of the flanges, however, is difficult to reconcile with Shang patterns. Flanges of this kind, with deeply undercut hooks, appear on early Western Chou bronzes such as the *Ch'eng Wang Ting* in Kansas City (Menzies, *ibid.*, No. 30; see also under No. 54 below), the *T'ai-pao Fang Ting* (T. Higuchi, *A New Study*, p. 111, fig. 36:6), and the Fogg Museum *Fang I* with curved beams like those of the *Yu* (No. 41) and with flanges very closely resembling those of the St. Louis *Lei* (*Shang Chou*, fig. 601; *Seika*, I, 43). The find from Li-chia-ts'un near Mei-hsien in Shensi, made in 1956, comprising several flanged vessels, suggests that by the middle of Western Chou this type of hooked flange had hopelessly degenerated (*KKHP*, XVI, 1957/2; T. Higuchi, *op. cit.*, 64–73). Accordingly, an early Western Chou date would seem probable, a date assumed also by Kidder. A similar *Lei* without lid is reproduced in *Tsun-ku-chai*, I/2, 28, 29.

44 CHIH OR TUAN
Western Chou?
H. 7½ in., DIAM. 3⅜ in.
Dr. Paul Singer, Summit, New Jersey

A graceful, slender goblet on a strongly flaring foot has incurved sides and a moderately widening mouth. The patina is fine, smooth, and greenish.
Not previously published.

This comparatively rare type appears to go back to the late Shang period. It was occasionally classed with the *Ku*, but its structure, especially the foot, differs widely from the *Ku*. Its commonest designation is *Chih*, which fits better but neglects the more elongated proportion of the present type. A few pieces of very similar shape excavated in Kiangsi Province in 1888 bear inscriptions giving the name of the vessel, *Tuan*, as well as that of the "maker," King I-ch'u of Hsü, a personage mentioned in the *Tso-chuan* under Chao Kung 6, or 536 B.C. (cf. Kuo Mo-jo, *Liang Chou*, 170: inscriptions, 207: one illustration; *ibidem*, K'ao-shih, 162: transcription of the longest of the three inscriptions; Jung Keng, *Shang Chou*, figs. 590, 591; Karlgren, *Yin and Chou*, C131). In two cases the inscriptions, incised on the outsides of the vessels, speak of "sacrificial *Tuan*," and the longer one explicitly states, in addition: ". . . to be used for offerings to august Heaven and to my accomplished late father; may he ever protect this person of mine; may sons and grandsons forever treasure it."

The lack of decoration makes it very difficult to come to a decision about the date of this type of vessel. Less tall variants designated as *Chih* in *Shang Chou* (figs. 582–584) are austerely decorated in Shang style. A comparatively ornate specimen with a frieze of birds and ogives in the Hellström collection, which looks very like a Shang bronze (see Karl-

gren, in *BMFEA*, XX, 1948, pl. 14:3), shows a more restrained flare of the mouth and a simple, conical foot. There are, however, no less than four plain goblets closely resembling our No. 44 in the former Liu T'i-chih collection, all inscribed in Shang manner (*Shan-chai*, ch. 4: 52, 59, 71, 85). The first of these pieces is now in the Hamburg Museum für Kunst und Gewerbe. Assigned to Shang or early Chou by Kristian Jakobsen ("Chinesische Bronzen," fig. 4 a–c), it bears an inscription on the outer bottom, a *ko* dagger-axe pictograph which, being cast in relief, favors a Shang date.

If this graceful and almost delicate type existed in Shang and Western Chou, it contrasted curiously with the heavily decorated and architectonically conceived vessels prevalent in those times. But it is no less curious that this type should have either persisted into, or suddenly reappeared during, the late Ch'un-ch'iu period, where the pieces of the prince of Hsü belong. Jakobsen, who believes that this type had become obsolete by the middle of the Chou period, seems willing to dismiss the Hsü inscriptions as spurious. Yet these inscriptions did pass the scrutiny of eminent Chinese connoisseurs and epigraphers such as Lo Chen-yü, Tsou An, Kuo Mo-jo, and Jung Keng; nor does Karlgren seem to have found any fault with them. There is an unsolved problem here, inviting speculation.

45　CHIH
Late Shang or early Chou, Style V
H. 5¹³⁄₁₆ in., W. 3¾ in.
City Art Museum of Saint Louis

This round beaker is of a rare type. The nearly cylindrical body rises from the cylindrical foot, bulging slightly below and curving slightly inward above. A faintly everted lip is set off by a constriction. The décor, in relief on a ground of rather large round spirals without barbs, is disposed in two zones. On the foot is a frieze in four sections, each of which is filled by two dragons whose bodies overlap and one of which is inverted. The tall frieze on the body is divided into four panels by carinate flanges, which are marked by chevrons alternating with bare stretches. In antithetical arrangement, these panels are occupied by configurations of large, long-necked birds with upright, involute tails, placed above T'ao-t'ieh masks of quite uncommon design. The relationship of birds and masks is such that the birds seem to function as parts of the masks, but the two are distinguished by their textures, the scaly plumage of the peacock-like birds contrasting with the smooth surface of the T'ao-t'ieh faces. Uncommon in the design of these faces are the formations of "forehead" and "nose" and "jaws," double eyebrows, the fusion of the "jaw" with a large claw toward the rear, beneath the smaller claw of the bird. The vessel is covered by a green patina and traces of a red pigment; incrustations of malachite and cuprite have formed on the inside.

Published: Kidder, *Early Chinese Bronzes*, pl. IV; City Art Museum *Bulletin*, XXXVI/1, 1951, fig. 7; *Handbook*, 1953, p. 250; *ACASA*, V, 1951, p. 76, fig. 19; *Yeh-chung p'ien-yü*, III, hsia: 2; Umehara, *Inkyo*, pl. 80:1.

The art-historically interesting features of this vessel, which Kidder characterized as "the most extraordinary bronze in the collection" of the St. Louis Museum (*op. cit.*, p. 38), are these: the overlapping and alternating inversion of the dragons; the tendency, recognizable in the design of the masks, toward curvilinear and large forms, involving a measure of disintegration of the traditional standards; and the ambiguity in the relationship of mask elements and bird elements. All these features suggest a very late Shang or post-Shang date.

The only comparable beaker to have come to the writer's attention was in the Peking art market early in 1945; its whereabouts are unknown.

46   P'AN
Probably early Western Chou
H. 4½ in., DIAM. 13¼ in.
The Minneapolis Institute of Arts; bequest of Alfred F. Pillsbury

A shallow, round basin, on a ring-foot splaying slightly toward the bottom, has a rim formed by a strong horizontal ledge. The outside is decorated with dragons and birds in two friezes. The meanders of the ground seem to be quite irregular, as their shapes and sizes follow the contours of the spaces they fill. Pairs of birds facing each other in the foot belt correspond to arcs occupied by two pairs of dragons in the much wider, upper belt. The center between these antithetically ordered dragons is marked by a buffalo head in high relief. The dragons, with bodies divided into plain strips, and with hooked extensions issuing from the curled tips of their upper tails, have long, hooked, involute beaks and large, extended claws. In addition they possess crests or plumes, behind their heads, which resemble the "antlers" with five prongs and eyes that are seen on the *Yu* from Boston and on the *Lei* from St. Louis (Nos. 41 and 43). The birds have enormously elongated tails supported in the middle by what looks very like a hind leg. In actuality this element, required by design in any case, corresponds to the down-curled part of the tail as seen in older representations, mimicking the shape of the bird's "foreleg." In the two friezes, the patina is gray-green.

Published: Karlgren, *Pillsbury Collection*, No. 38.

The element that speaks most decidedly in favor of a post-Shang date is the five-pronged "antler," or "bottle horn with fingerleaf top" in Karlgren's description, which surely must be derived from such versions as seen in Nos. 41 and 43. If these prototypes are correctly ascribed to the end of Shang and the beginning of Western Chou, respectively, the derivative version in the Minneapolis *P'an* is unlikely to be earlier than early Chou. Nor is this estimate contradicted by the rest of the ornaments. The buffalo head, as pointed out by Karlgren, is "unusually realistic," which means that it is unusual by Shang standards. The smooth and sleek bodies of both dragons and birds, too, without a remnant of curl or spiral in them, appear to require an early Chou rather than Shang date.

47 TSUN
Late Shang or early Chou
H. 9⅞ in., DIAM. (at mouth) 7¹⁵⁄₁₆ in.
The Cleveland Museum of Art; purchase from the J. H. Wade Fund

This stout beaker has a conical foot that flares strongly at its molded base, a moderately convex middle part, and a more strongly outcurved upper part. Compact and smoothly outlined flanges divide the sides into four quadrants. Broadening subtly on approaching the top, they jut out beyond the rim with irrepressible momentum. The vessel is decorated in five superposed bands and in four tall ogives above them, and the various motifs are done in bold relief on a ground of rather small, rounded spirals. On the foot there are two T'ao-t'ieh masks whose eyes, eyebrows, and inner parts of the horns stand out plastically from the masks' surfaces. The outer parts of their horns are distinguished by pointed hooks. On the middle section of the vessel are two friezes, showing two birds in each panel, which are separated by a band of vertical ribs between the friezes. In the panels of the next zone we find single dragons facing their counterparts in the adjoining panels. The ogives, halved by the upper flanges, are filled with T'ao-t'ieh masks like those on the foot, but smaller and facing upward, above which are triangular figures of grooved bands with barbs and volutes. There is a smooth patina of a greenish turquoise tone, overgrown by malachite crusts and patches of cuprite, and a heavy incrustation in the interior. On the inner bottom is a cast inscription of six characters reading, *tso Fu Mou pao tsun-i*, "made for Father Mou this precious tsun-i."

Published: H. C. Hollis, "A Chinese Sacrificial Wine Vessel," C.M.A. *Bulletin*, December 1938, 176, 177; *ibidem*, July 1939, p. 127; P. Ackerman, *Ritual Bronzes of Ancient China*, pl. 36.

A surprisingly similar vessel of about the same size in the collection of H. E. Alexander J. Argyropoulos was exhibited in the Palazzo Ducale in Venice, 1954 (Dubosc, *Mostra d'Arte Cinese*, No. 22, pl. 3). Its décor, unobscured by the marvelously smooth patina, agrees panel for panel with that of the Cleveland vase, deviating only in small details. The only significant difference lies in the shape of the heads of the four flanges in the Cleveland vase, where the heads are broadened and end with a sloping plane and short downward extension: a beautiful solution that contributes much toward "the architectonic semblance of the flanges," as perceptively stated in Hollis' description.

The feature of the band of vertical ribs circling the middle calls to mind such vessels as the two *Yu*, Nos. 40 and 41, and the older Pao-chi set in the Metropolitan Museum. In addition to the *Yu* with vertical ribs, this set comprises a large *Tsun* showing similar, though obtrusively heavy and somewhat exaggerated, flanges. Compared to this *Tsun* there is a notable restraint in the design of the Cleveland vase. (For the Pao-chi *Tsun*, see Umehara, *Seika*, I, 2; *idem*, *Henkin*, pl. 4; Jung Keng, *Shang Chou*, fig. 500). Viewed in the light of these stylistic associations, the Cleveland piece may yet prove to be a Shang work. Moreover, two important *Tsun* which by virtue of their inscriptions are unquestionable early Chou monuments, the *Ch'en Ch'en Tsun* and the *Nieh Ling Fang Tsun* (*Shang Chou*, figs. 536 and 554), display flanges of a different kind, with deeply undercut openwork hooks.

48 KUEI
Early Western Chou
H. 10¾ in., DIAM. (at mouth) 8⅝ in.
Fogg Art Museum, Harvard University, Cambridge, Massachusetts

A round bowl, with two handles of heavy proportions, is cast in one piece with the square pedestal. The relief décor, in plain and convex, double-layered relief, stands forth against a ground of finely executed spirals. On both pedestal and bowl appear large T'ao-t'ieh masks with C-shaped horns, outward curved mouths that bare two fangs, and pointed, leaf-shaped ears. The mask on the base is flanked by dragon figures with turned heads, mushroom horns, and tall, blade-shaped crests; in the upper one the upcurved bands of the T'ao-t'ieh body fill the spaces between mask and handles. On the forehead shield of each mask sits an angular, protruding animal head with horns. The corresponding sections of the foot belt contain pairs of addorsed birds that face the birds in the adjoining sections. At the top of the handles are animal heads modeled in the round and surmounted by shield-like horns in a vertical position. Below these heads, the handle is shaped as the winged body of a bird whose head is invisible, while its claws and tail are shown in low relief on the sides of the large, rectangular plaques that are attached to the lower part of the handles. The vessel has a greenish gray surface of silvery sheen, with spotty crusts of oxide, russet, and green.

On the inner bottom of the bowl, an inscription of eleven characters is cast in intaglio, reading as follows: *Wang i Tê pei, nien p'eng, yung tso pao tsun-i*, "The king gave Tê cowries, twenty strings, wherefore he (Tê) had this precious sacrificial vessel made."

Published: Umehara, *Seika*, II, 110; *Exhibition of Ancient Chinese Bronzes and Buddhist Art*, Yamanaka & Co., New York, 1938, p. 48, No. 29; Umehara, *Henkin*, p. 20, fig. 4; Ch'en Meng-chia, in *KKHP*, X, 1955, p. 108, fig. 13, pl. 16; Watson, *Ancient Chinese Bronzes*, pl. 37a; T. Higuchi, "A New Study on Western Chou Bronzes," pp. 13–15, fig. 3; Loehr, *Symbols and Images*, Wellesley College, 1967, No. 5.

At last we are faced with a specimen safely datable within narrow limits. This *Kuei* is one of four vessels made for the same person, Tê, whose name recurs in the inscription of each—once in connection with a sacrifice performed by the king at Ch'eng Chou for Wu Wang, founder of the Chou Dynasty. The four vessels are

1. a round *Ting* in the Shanghai Museum, with the same inscription as on the Fogg Museum *Kuei*, No. 48 (*Shanghai Museum Bronzes*, No. 14);
2. a square *Ting* in the Shanghai Museum, with an inscription referring to the sacrifice for Wu Wang (*Shanghai Museum Bronzes*, No. 28);
3. a pedestaled *Kuei* in the Fogg Museum, with an inscrip-

tion recording the king's gift of ten serfs, ten strings of cowries and one hundred sheep (Ch'en Meng-chia, in *KKHP*, X, p. 108, fig. 12, pls. 17, 18; Higuchi, "A New Study," p. 13, under *Shu Tê Kuei*, pl. 1:2);

4. the pedestaled *Kuei* in our exhibition, No. 48.

Ch'en Meng-chia assigns the Fogg Museum bronzes to the reign of Ch'eng Wang. Higuchi confirms this date in view of the close stylistic and thematic connection of No. 3 with early Chou bronzes such as the *T'ien Wu Kuei* and the *Chung Ch'eng Kuei* in the Art Institute of Chicago (see commentary to No. 50 below), and in any case rules out a date later than K'ang Wang.

49   KUEI
Western Chou
H. 6¼ in., W. 12 in.
The Minneapolis Institute of Arts; bequest of Alfred F. Pillsbury

This round bowl with curved sides and flaring mouth stands on a conical foot-ring with molded base. The two handles are rounded in section and covered with an ornament of sunken spirals with curved barbs; they are surmounted by animal heads in relief, and carry appendages in the form of outward curling hooks. The decoration of the vessel consists of a very narrow belt on the foot and a wide one on the wall, both executed in flat relief on a ground of finely drawn spirals of varying sizes. Around the foot runs the geometric pattern called "eyed band with diagonals" by Karlgren, with the eye placed in the middle of the arc between the handles. The frieze on the wall is filled with magnificent, large bird figures with turned heads, placed antithetically. From the birds' curved and upswept body-and-wing, tail feathers issue and, turning at right angles, fall in four separate strands. Two of these strands are ornamented with circles as though to suggest the eyes of peacocks' feathers. The birds themselves are adorned with plumes of like kind. But the grandiose character of the design at large results from the bold duplication of these plumes in two separate strands which, springing from a disengaged volute above the birds' bodies, sweep up and forward above their heads and down between them. "Pale green patina with patches of blue-green," is Karlgren's description of the color.

The vessel bears an inscription of forty-three characters plus two reduplicates. The inscription says:

"It was when the King, having subdued Chi-yü(?) and gone to subdue Nao-hei(?), on his return performed a *liao* (sacrifice) at Tsung Chou, that he presented (me) Kuo Po Kua with ten strings of cowries. (I) presume to announce that in praise of the King's grace I have this precious sacrificial *Kuei* made for my accomplished deceased father. May for a myriad of years sons and grandsons forever treasure and use it."

Published: The Minneapolis Institute of Arts *Bulletin*, XXXVII/14, April 13, 1948; Karlgren, "Yin and Chou," B186; *idem, Pillsbury Collection*, No. 36; *Cheng-sung-t'ang*, pu-i shang, 26 b; *San-tai*, 8:50; Ferguson's *Index*, p. 595.

The décor of this beautiful *Kuei*, which is said to have come from Hsi-an in Shensi, recurs in two bronzes bearing inscriptions of a prince of Ching: *Yu* (*Senoku Seishō*, II, 67; rev. ed., No. 79, not illustrated; Higuchi, "A New Study," fig. 35:2) and *Tsun* (*Ku Kung t'ung-ch'i*, II, shang 110; Higuchi, fig. 35:1; details in T'an Tan-ch'iung, *Decorative Patterns in Chinese Bronzes*, pl. 35).

The date of this *Kuei* is unlikely to be earlier than the time of K'ang Wang and the following reigns, as considered for the two *Tsun* with comparable bird ornament from Philadelphia and Princeton, Nos. 51 and 52.

A variant design of birds standing face to face, with the splendorous shower of their dentate, eyeless plumes in six strands between them, appears on a *Yu* in the Freer Gallery of Art (No. 47.12). Possibly this design preceded the peacock theme of No. 49 and the vessels from Ching.

50   KUANG
Predynastic Chou, coeval with Shang Style V
H. 12⅜ in., L. 14³⁄₁₆ in.
The Art Museum, Princeton University

Although of the same class as No. 34 and probably not far apart in time, this vessel with its dark, shiny patina seems alien among the Shang vessels discussed under No. 34. Most distinctive is the shape of the foot, a truncated pyramid with a base of conspicuous plainness. The body is rectangular and the corners are accentuated by spurred flanges such as those that divide the long sides of the body. Shorter flanges without spurs are in corresponding positions on the foot, level with the décor zone. The recessed and flaring register above the rectangular body has rounded corners, and the lid with its head of an animal with mushroom horns in front, and a high relief mask with upright horns and a prominent "tongue" in the rear, does not essentially differ from Shang designs. It is in the decoration that we become aware, again, of an element scarcely compatible with Shang tradition. The same bird motif is repeated, with slight variations as necessitated by the given dimensions of the compartments, through all registers. And, the design of these birds is strange indeed. All along their tails and plumes sit rows of sharp points or barbs; small straight darts project rearward from their heads. Their bodies and wings have shrunk to a few concentric curves below their heads. A very heavy loop handle has the form of a monster with wide open mouth, swallowing or emitting a large bird figure, in the round, with a spiked crest in front.

The vessel bears an inscription of six characters: "Wen fu Ting," followed by the formula conventionally read "hsi tzu sun."

Published: *Fujita Danshaku-ke zōhin nyūsatsu mokuroku*, Osaka, 1929, No. 233; Umehara, *Nihon Seika*, III, 263; *idem*, "The Second Set of Ritual Vessels, *Pien-chin*, from Pao-chi-hsien," p. 8, fig. 2; *Archives of Asian Art*, XX, 1966/67, p. 101, fig. 45.

According to Umehara, this *Kuang* is related to the bronzes of the hoard known as the "second set from Pao-chi-hsien," of which the *Yu*, No. 41, forms a part.

A very similar specimen is in the Brundage collection (d'Argencé, *Brundage Bronzes*, pl. 21 A), which appears to differ only on three counts: the birds' spiky frills are rendered less sparingly; the birds' beaks are closed; the spurs of the flanges are treated with more restraint.

The connection of the two *Kuang* with the Pao-chi bronzes hinges on a pedestaled *Kuei* in that hoard, which is decorated with bird figures of the same design (Umehara, "The Second Set," pl. 2:2, side view; Watson, *Ancient Chinese Bronzes*, pl. 32, front view). The bird pattern appears also on a *Ting* in the British Museum (Watson, *ibid.*, pl. 44a; rubbings of the pattern in Umehara, "The Second Set," pl. 5:2). All these vessels with the spiky bird pattern would seem to have come from the same foundry and to be synchronous. They are stylistically consistent and almost uniform. An interesting detail in the décor of the *Kuei* is the contrasting design of the smaller birds at the foot and at the neck: they are of unadulterated Shang style, without spikes, but with short crests, and with full-size wings. This contrast makes the strange character of the large, spiky birds even more obvious: their wings reduced to a few concentric curves below the head, they consist virtually of head, crest, and tail only. Moreover, crests and tails are so assimilated that they speak as units of a pattern rather than organic parts. Seen side by side with the small, graceful Shang birds, the spiky pattern has an undeniably uncouth touch.

The relationship to the "second set" does not imply that the group here discussed is securely datable. For the set, so called, was not originally designed as a set, as rightly pointed out by Umehara ("The Second Set," English summary, p.

iv). The dates have to be worked out for each particular style and type. Umehara believes the Princeton *Kuang* to be the oldest of its type and possibly still of Shang date (*Nihon Seika*, III, 263), whereas he assumes an early Chou date for the Brundage piece (*ibidem*, 264). I see no valid reason for separating them. Both must be either Shang or Chou, but possibly predynastic Chou.

The pedestal of a *Kuei* in the Art Institute of Chicago, of early Western Chou date, is decorated with bird figures clearly derived from the spiky birds on the *Kuei* mentioned above. A flame-like, four-pronged device replaces the spiky plume, and the birds' heads are altered so as to resemble small elephant heads (Kelley and Ch'en, *Chinese Bronzes from the Buckingham Collection*, pls. 20–22; *Tsun-ku-chai*, I/2:9; *Shang Chou*, fig. 290). Bowl and handles virtually duplicate those of the important *T'ien Wu Kuei* whose inscription, mentioning a sacrifice for Wen Wang, dates from the time of Wu Wang, the founder of the Chou Dynasty (Jung Keng, *Shang Chou*, fig. 298). It is not impossible that this *Kuei* was cast before the Chou conquest (*Wen-wu*, 1958/1, p. 29 ff; cf. Watson, *Ancient Chinese Bronzes*, p. 49 f.). The early Chou date of the *T'ien Wu Kuei* is supported by a similarly decorated *Kuei* in the Fogg Museum inscribed by one Tê, a companion piece to No. 48 in our exhibition, datable to Ch'eng Wang's reign. It cannot seriously be doubted that the *Kuei* from Pao-chi which shows the spiky birds in their earlier form precedes the Chicago *Kuei*. If the latter dates, as convincingly argued by Ch'en Meng-chia, from "the earliest days of the reign of Ch'eng Wang" (*Buckingham Bronzes*, p. 150), the former would almost certainly fall to the time before Wu Wang's short reign of three years, that is, the time before the conquest. The two *Kuang* vessels related to the Pao-chi *Kuei*, therefore, are likely to antedate the fall of Shang.

51 TSUN
Early Western Chou
H. 9½ in., DIAM. (at mouth) 8¼ in.
University Museum, University of Pennsylvania, Philadelphia

The flaring rim is the widest part of this stout goblet with curving sides, which rests on a splayed foot. There are three zones of ornament, effectively contrasting with the plain foot. The main zone, around the belly, shows two pairs of addorsed birds with their heads turned, large figures rendered in sweeping concentric curves in relief on *lei-wen* ground. Below their prominent, round eyes appears the common scale-like sign. Their beaks are transformed into big volutes whose rotating motion is answered by the bold curves formed by their crests and plumes. Above this zone is a narrow band of small, dragon-like figures; with turned and crested heads, and with bodies conforming to recumbent S-curves, they are assimilated, to some degree, to the design of the birds. Broad ogival leaves of ornament, separated by smooth gussets, stretch from the narrow band to the rim. Each of these leaves is filled by a pair of confronted figures consisting of barbed, curving, grooved bands running parallel to the contours of the leaves; bifurcating below, the bands terminate in heads resembling the birds' heads but placed upside down, and barbed crests which join the heads from below. Two feline heads in high relief accentuate the middle axis at the level of the narrow dragon belt. The surface is distinguished by a smooth, glossy, and blackish patina of striking beauty, resembling the lustrous black patination of late Eastern Chou and Han mirrors and presumably caused by a high tin content of the alloy.

An inscription of four characters, *tso pao tsun-i*, "made [this] precious sacrificial vessel," is noteworthy insofar as palaeographically it points to an early Western Chou date.

Published: Umehara, *Seika*, I, 27; *idem*, *Kodōki keitai*, pl. 8:10; Jung Keng, *Shang Chou*, II, fig. 545.

The date of this resplendent vessel, the decoration of which exemplifies to perfection one stylistic tendency that emerged after Ch'eng Wang's time, depends on a series of similarly decorated bronzes bearing inscriptions which point to the reign of K'ang Wang at the earliest. This series, widely discussed in Chinese epigraphic works and reviewed in Karlgren's "Yin and Chou" under B35–B40, comprises the following items:

Keng Ying Yu (Fogg Museum); Ch'en Meng-chia in *KKHP*, XI, 1956, No. 55, pls. 9, 10, dating it to K'ang Wang's time in agreement with Kuo Mo-jo, *K'ao-shih*, 43a, and Wu Ch'i-ch'ang; cf. Karlgren, B61.

Hsiao Tsun (Hakuzuru Museum); *Hakkaku*, pl. 9; Jung Keng, *Shang Chou*, fig. 544; Ch'en Meng-chia in *KKHP*, XIII, 1956, No. 62; Kuo Mo-jo, *op. cit.*, 101, under Hsiao Wang; Karlgren, B36, pl. 21.

Hsiao Yu, related to the preceding item; Kuo Mo-jo, *Liang Chou t'u-lu*, fig. 175, *K'ao-shih*, 101b; Karlgren, B35.

Ching Kuei and *Ching Yu*; Kuo, *Liang Chou*, figs. 63 and 169, *K'ao-shih*, 55b and 56a, under Mu Wang; Ch'en, in *KKHP*, XI, 1956, p. 93, under K'ang Wang or Chao Wang; Karlgren, B160 and 161.

Shih T'ang-fu Ting (formerly Liu T'i-chih collection, now National Central Museum, Taipei; T'an, *Decorative Patterns*, pl. 36; *Ku Kung t'ung-ch-i*, No. 79); Jung Keng, *Shang Chou*, fig. 58; *idem*, *Shan-chai t'u-lu*, 35; Kuo, *K'ao-shih*, 70; Ch'en, *KKHP*, XIV, 1956, No. 85; Karlgren, B55; Higuchi, "A New Study," pl. 36:7. The latest in the series, this *Ting* is assigned to the reign of Kung Wang (ca. 927–908) by Kuo as well as Ch'en. Its imposing but dry design of large birds has lost the grace and vigor we admire in the Philadelphia goblet, which may well go back to K'ang Wang's time (ca. 1004–985).

52   TSUN
Early Western Chou
H. 6⅞₁₆ in., DIAM. (at mouth) 6¹¹⁄₁₆ in.
The Art Museum, Princeton University

This goblet with splayed foot, curved sides, and flaring mouth is similar to No. 51. The décor is arranged in the same order as in No. 51, and the foot, too, is left plain. But in details of the design, interesting differences will be noted. The bands marking the central axis between the confronted birds of the main zone are not plumes issuing from the birds' heads but extensions of their wings, boldly sweeping around the heads and downward. Similar curved bands extend rearward from the birds' tails. The birds' beaks, however, are not transformed into large volutes like those of the Philadelphia *Tsun*. Long-tailed birds take the place of the dragons in the neck-zone. In the ogives above the neck-zone there are broad, grooved bands conforming to the outline and ending in volutes bent inward, with barbs and pointed hooks filling the spaces below the volutes; there are no zoomorphic formations. Two small, sculptured heads are placed in the neck band above each confronted pair of the big birds. The surface is covered by a superb, smooth, green patina.

Published: *The Carl Otto von Kienbusch, Jr., Memorial Collection*, The Art Museum, Princeton University, Special Exhibition Catalogue, June 1956, No. 135.

The striking motif of the big bird in curvilinear figuration occurs in variants other than those exemplified by the Princeton and Philadelphia goblets. An outstanding instance of design is offered in the variant of the Pillsbury collection in Minneapolis (Karlgren, No. 29), which resembles the design of the *Ching Yu* (Kuo Mo-jo, *Liang Chou*, fig. 169), mentioned under No. 51 above. The *Ching Kuei* (*ibidem*, fig. 63; Jung Keng, *Shang Chou*, II, fig. 271), on the other hand, contemporaneous with the *Yu*, is decorated with the bird motif of the Philadelphia *Tsun*. A fourth, roughly contemporaneous variant presents itself in the *Hsiao Tsun* (*Hakkaku*, 9). In view of these variations within the same style, the attempt to establish their exact sequence would seem premature for the present. It is important, however, to recognize the stylistic principles common to the designs in question.

The tendency toward large, coherent, curved, and smoothly flowing units of design is obvious. As a consequence the motifs, birds in this case, remain significant only to the extent that they afford that curvilinear flow. Less obvious is the inevitable effect of this tendency on the nature of the ornaments in general. The transformations of the simple image into curvilinear configurations bring about an assimilation of the parts: the beak becomes crest-like, the crest, tail-like. The image, therefore, is destined to submerge in a pattern. In the end, there will be unified patterns.

53 LI
Early Western Chou
H. 5¾ in., w. 6⅛ in.
Museum of Fine Arts, Boston; Grace M. Edwards Fund

A tripod with three hollow legs stands on short, perpendicular, round and solid feet. Above the bulging lobes of the body is a contraction, topped by a slightly flaring rim which supports two upright handles. The décor covers the body without horizontal divisions, conforming to the three lobes; only the feet are left bare. Three times repeated, centered on the legs and bulges, is a T'ao-t'ieh mask of separated parts in relief on a ground of mainly rounded spirals. The design comprises unusual elements, among which may be noted three: the eyed hooks of the forehead shield; the plain stripes curving out from the bases of the C-shaped horns and descending vertically on either side of the forehead shield, dissecting the mask; and horizontally striped bands or legs(?) with long claws pointing upward at either side of the mask. There is a smooth and shiny greenish patina.

The vessel bears an inscription of thirteen characters, revealing the origin and date of this vessel; first deciphered by Ch'en Meng-chia, it says:

> "Prince Hsi of Lu had this *I* made to be used for offerings of cooked food to his accomplished late father, the Duke of Lu."

Hsi was the personal name of the fourth Duke of the Lu principality in western Shantung, who reigned as Yang Kung for six years after his elder brother's, K'ao Kung's, short reign of four years. Both were sons of Po Ch'in, who served under K'ang Wang, and grandsons of the Duke of Chou. The inscription, therefore, dates from the end of K'ang Wang's or from Chao Wang's reign. In Ch'en's computation, Yang Kung's reign spanned the years 994–989 B.C.

Published: Ch'en Meng-chia, in *AA*, X, 1947, 106, 107; *idem*, in *KKHP*, XI, 1956/1, 83, 84; Mizuno, *Bronzes and Jades*, pl. 91; *idem*, in *OA*, V/4, 1959, fig. 44.

While there seems to exist no closely comparable vessel, the feature of the plain strips bracketing eyes and eyebrows of the mask does call to mind the décor of the *Fang I* from the Metropolitan Museum, No. 56, whose T'ao-t'ieh design appears to represent a boldly simplified variation of the present one. A smaller detail, the eyes in the hooks of the forehead shields, may be compared with what resemble small eyes at the tips of the tail feathers of the large birds on the Princeton *Tsun*, No. 52.

54 FANG TING
Early Western Chou
H. (including handles) 10¼ in., w. 7⅜ in., D. 6 in.
Avery Brundage Collection, M. H. de Young Memorial Museum, San Francisco

This tetrapod with rectangular cauldron is covered by a smooth, gray-green patina. Strong, spiked flanges accentuate the corners and the centers of each of the four sides of the vessel, halving the T'ao-t'ieh masks which fill the sides. The masks are cast in relief on a ground pattern of squarish meanders. These masks with their oval, slit eyes, inward-curved lips, pointed ears and eyebrows, hardly differ from late Shang designs. The feature that distinguishes them from Shang styles is the form of their "horns" or, rather, plumes, flamboyantly curving about the faces and recurving at the tips. These plumes are very large and smoothly flowing forms which greatly alter the general character of the ornament, and their flow is further enhanced by two parallel grooves running along the middle. Their outer contours are lined with a plain, jagged and barbed crest in slightly lower relief. Another feature setting this vessel's design apart from Shang design is the presence of full-round, small, horned monsters which climb up the sides of the arched handles and stare at each other from round, bulging eyes: quadrupeds of rather eager and energetic appearance, of a fanciful species that may have originated with some late Shang zoomorphic design transposed into sculpture. More conventional are the masks attached like capitals to the plain, nearly cylindrical feet.

The vessel bears an inscription of thirty-two characters in six columns, which may be translated as follows:

> It was in the second moon, the first quarter, on the day *keng-yin*, at Tsung Chou, when Lu(?) Chung presented his liegeman(?) X with a pair of chariot feather-pennants and a horse. To extol my lord's graciousness I had made for Chi Kung this treasured Tsun-i.

Published: d'Argencé, *Brundage Bronzes*, pl. XXIX. Cf. Ch'en Meng-chia, in *KKHP*, X, 1955, p. 107, pl. 11.

The maker of this remarkable vessel was a "serf" of high station, in Ch'en Meng-chia's opinion; Chi Kung, for whom the vessel was made, presumably was his deceased father. The inscription is meant to inform the maker's departed ancestors; at the same time it was expected to be seen by his descendants, who are admonished to "treasure" this vessel.

There are at least three *Fang-ting* to compare. Two of them show the same kind of small animals on the handles: the *Ch'eng Wang Ting* in the Nelson Gallery, Kansas City, which most probably dates from the time of K'ang Wang (*An Exhibition of Ancient Chinese Ritual Bronzes Loaned by C. T. Loo*, The Detroit Institute of Arts, 1940, pl. 18; Bachhofer, *A Short History*, pl. 17; S. Lee, *A History of Far Eastern Art*, 1964, p. 40, fig. 29), and the *T'ai-pao Ting*, ascribed to the early K'ang Wang period by Ch'en Meng-chia (*KKHP*, X, 1955,

pl. 12). A similar T'ao-t'ieh of slightly stiffer and less rich design appears on a vessel with plain handles, the *Hou Ch'o Fang-ting*, whose inscription has been dealt with in many epigraphic repertories. This decorated vessel is reproduced in Jung Keng's *Shang Chou* (Vol. II, fig. 138), where it is assigned to Early Western Chou (*ibid.*, Vol. I, p. 309); a date in Ch'eng Wang's reign is advocated by Kuo Mo-jo (*Liang Chou, K'ao-shih*, 29b) as well as Ch'en Meng-chia (*KKHP*, X, 1955, p. 110), who, however, admits that the case is beset with an authenticity problem insofar as the Sung illustration in *Hsü K'ao-ku-t'u* shows a plain vessel bearing the same inscription.

On the strength of the two analogues mentioned before, a date in the K'ang Wang period would seem plausible.

55 FANG TING
Early Western Chou
H. (including handles) 11 in., W. 8¹¹⁄₁₆ in., D. 8⅞ in.
Kunstindustrimuseum, Copenhagen

A tetrapod, consisting of a rectangular cauldron with tall, loop handles and vertical, spurred flanges at the corners and in the middle of the four sides, is carried by rather slender, cylindrical legs. An incised ornament of long, narrow lancets with curled ends below horizontally placed spirals adorns the legs. The sides are occupied by large, flamboyantly drawn T'ao-t'ieh masks in layered relief on a ground of fine, rounded and angular spirals. The masks, whose proportions vary in accordance with the dimensions of the panels, are flanked by dragons in headlong position. Most striking in these masks is the formation of the horns, whose recumbent C-shapes are enriched at their upper contours by curved hooks and prongs resembling licking flames, and are extended laterally by large, involute curls. Some features of the masks that differ from older designs deserve to be mentioned: the ears have short, upward extensions curved outward; the eyebrows are striated and without hooks; the eyes, strongly protuberant, approach the shape of a cone. The outer faces of the handles are marked by two sunken, concentric grooves. On the under side of the bottom are diagonally crossed, molded ribs. The surface shows a shiny, grayish patina with green incrustations. A cast inscription of eight characters says, according to the lenders' kindly furnished information:

"Lady Wu of Chi made this precious *Ting*." (Chi is one of the Chou clan names.)

Published: N. Palmgren, "Exhibition of Early Chinese Bronzes, Stockholm, 1933," *BMFEA*, VI, 1934, pl. 11:2; The Karlbeck Syndicate 1931–32, 1933, No. 659; Feddersen, *Chinesisches Kunstgewerbe*, 1939, fig. 83; Exhibition, Kunstindustrimuseum 1950, No. 33; Ny Carlsbergfondets Jubilaeumsudstilling, 1952, No. 624; André Leth, *Chinese Art*, 1959, No. 16; Karlgren, "Marginalia II," *BMFEA*, XXXII, 1960, pl. 1a.

Two similar *Fang Ting* exist, one in the Seligman Collection (S. H. Hansford, *Seligman Collection*, A 3, pl. 2), the other in the Winthrop collection, Fogg Art Museum (Umehara, *Inkyo*, pl. 70:1). As noted by Hansford, the décor of these two vessels is virtually identical. Yet it differs sufficiently from that of the Copenhagen specimen to enable us to come to a decision about their chronological relationship. The chief differences are these:

1. the horns, which in No. 55 still show a basic C-shape with the lateral extensions distinctly recognizable as appendages, are fused into coherent bodies in the other vessels, where the tips of the "C" are reduced to a curl;

2. the flame-like hooks along the upper edge of the C-horn in No. 55 are larger than the hooks on the sides, whereas in the other vessels this differentiation has disappeared; there, all the hooks are of equal size and rhythmically uniform throughout;

3. the ears of the T'ao-t'ieh in No. 55 still have the shape of an ear comparable to the leaf-shape common in Shang V and early Western Chou, but, as mentioned above, they have upward extensions curving outward—thus assuming an S-shape quite analogous to the transformation of the horns; in the other vessels this complex form is replaced by a simpler one, like a big inverted comma, and assimilated to the form of the involute jaws.

Since these differences betray the same tendency in modifying given forms or form complexes, they are symptomatic of a subtle stylistic shift; therefore, they count chronologically. But the Copenhagen vessel's décor, slightly closer to older styles and thus unquestionably a little earlier than the Seligman and Fogg Museum designs, is itself informed by the tendency observed in the latter two. And, it is because of this general similarity of the formal properties that the differences are subtle ones.

The affinity of No. 55 to older styles need not be discussed at length. A perfect older example of this tetrapod class to compare is the *Tê Fang Ting* in Shanghai (*Shanghai Museum Bronzes*, No. 28), mentioned under No. 48 above, a vessel whose inscription refers to an offering to Wu Wang and therefore warrants an early Western Chou date, most likely in Ch'eng Wang's reign. In this vessel, the feature of the "licking flames" above the T'ao-t'ieh horns is present, but the hooks are stiff, angular, sparse, and compatible with Shang tradition. In that regard, the Brundage *Fang Ting*, No. 54, despite its drastically altered, plume-like horns, shows no change either. If the K'ang Wang date assumed for No. 54 is correct, the date of No. 55 ought to be later. In fact, the mask designs of an outstanding bronze monument of the Chao Wang period, the *Ling Fang I* (*Freer Gallery Bronzes*, pls. 21, 22), and of stylistically related bronzes of the same type in the Nezu Museum (Mizuno, *Bronzes and Jades*, pl. 105) and in Chicago (*Buckingham Bronzes*, pls. 24–26) show "all of a sudden" the kind of conspicuous prongs above the horns which lead straight toward the more advanced formulation of the Copenhagen specimen. In these *Fang I* masks, the ears, too, are redesigned, with extensions upward and inward. Accordingly, the Copenhagen tetrapod may date from the later years of Chao Wang or from the beginning of Mu Wang's long reign, which may still accommodate the Seligman and Winthrop pieces compared above.

56   FANG I
Early Western Chou
H. 11 in., W. 7 in., D. 6 in.
The Metropolitan Museum of Art, New York City; Rogers Fund, 1943

A roof-shaped lid with a roof-shaped knob covers this rectangular vessel with flaring, molded foot and rim. In contrast to precursors described earlier (Nos. 37 and 38), the sides of this vessel bulge and undulate, and the lid is more noticeably convex. The crests or flanges, along the corners and down the middle of the sides, are dissected at the levels of the plain strips which separate the décor zones; on the body they are further accentuated by blunt spurs. The decoration is done in low, sharp-edged relief on a ground of shallow, loosely rendered spirals. A T'ao-t'ieh of unusual design appears as the main motif on the eight sides of body and lid. It is rendered in separated parts (as in the older vessel No. 37 of the Frederick M. Mayer collection), with oval, lidless eyes, the face being distinguished by the bold, sweeping, curves in which the "nose," forehead shield, and involute horns coalesce. Not a single spiral is left in these parts; they are drawn in flat, plain bands with a groove in the middle. The eyebrows are dislocated, swept into a vertical position in accord with the curved tips of the horns. Twenty identical dragon figures, rendered in plain bands, fill the compartments of the friezes above and below the belly and along the ridge of the lid. In the frieze around the neck, a small feline head in high relief takes the place of the corresponding flange sections. The inscription consists of a single cast glyph which has not yet been deciphered; see Jung Keng, *Chin-wen-pien*, 1939, fu-lu, shang 48a; *ibidem*, 1959, p. 894.

Published: Umehara, *Seika*, I, 44; *Chinese Bronzes*, The Metropolitan Museum of Art, 1938, No. 107; Jung Keng, *Shang Chou*, fig. 599; Priest, "Chinese Bronzes," p. 106.

This *Fang I* is one of a group of three bronzes linked by their décor and identical inscriptions. The other two are a *Kuang* in the Metropolitan Museum (*Seika*, II, 146; *Shang Chou*, fig. 682 a–d; J. Trübner, *Yu und Kuang*, pls. 52–55) and a *Tsun* beaker in Minneapolis (*Seika*, I, 17; *Shang Chou*, fig. 551; Karlgren, *Pillsbury Collection*, No. 27). Discussing this group in his paper on "Some Early Chinese Bronze Masters," *BMFEA*, XVI, 1944, p. 14, *s.v.* Group X, Karlgren judged the décor to be done "in a forcible, first-class Yin A style."

The items Nos. 37, 38, and 56 in our exhibition form a highly instructive, telling sequence, in which No. 56 is the latest of the three. It is in sequences of this kind that we can become aware of the form-consciousness or the artistic thought of the ancient designers. In the shaping of the vessels and their expressive flanges we can contemplate the increasing concern with articulate structures. We also observe a gradually lessened importance of the rôle of the detail within each unit of design such as the dragon figures, or the horns of the T'ao-t'ieh. But specifically, as regards the ornament of the Metropolitan Museum piece, No. 56, we note that not only have the dragons become somewhat plain and impoverished elements, but also its T'ao-t'ieh is in jeopardy, as the long inviolate features have become the object of new experiments in design.

57   LI
Middle Western Chou
H. 9 in., DIAM. 10⅞ in.
The Cleveland Museum of Art; John L. Severance Fund.

This sturdy tripod with hollow, short, bulging legs and contracted neck has a flaring rim which supports two upright handles. Save for the feet, the surface is covered with ornaments in low relief on *lei-wen* ground. T'ao-t'ieh faces, dissolved into curving, grooved bands, occupy the three bulges. The same kind of band is used for the elements in the frieze around the neck, remnants of dragons and related zoomorphous motifs, now dissected and deprived of their quasi-organic character. The patina on the outside, according to a description given by Wai-kam Ho, is smooth and even gray-green, with patches of mottled white probably caused by tin oxide; the inside is gray-green but shows small areas of blank metal and earthy incrustation. The vessel, which bears no inscription, reportedly came from Hsi-an, Shensi.

Published: Cleveland Museum of Art *Bulletin*, November, 1961, p. 235; *ACASA*, XVI, 1962, p. 106, fig. 7; Chêng Tê-k'un, *Chou China*, pl. 20a; Wai-kam Ho, "Shang and Chou Bronzes," C.M.A. *Bulletin*, September, 1964, 174–187, ill. p. 182; *Handbook* of the C.M.A., 1966, p. 245; *Selected Works*, The C.M.A., 1967, pl. 50.

The derivation of the T'ao-t'ieh designs from Early Western Chou prototypes is readily seen and unproblematic. Interesting from the point of view of form is the calculated disarray of the parts through the arbitrary introduction of freely moving bands which cut asunder, and destroy, the once coherent faces. Unity, in this new design, depends strongly on the uniformity of the bands, all of which are of equal width and marked by median grooves. A revealing comparison can be made with the early Western Chou *Li* from the Boston Museum, No. 53, where we observe the beginnings of a transformation of the T'ao-t'ieh design.

In a careful investigation of the designs on approximately datable vessels of early, middle, and late Western Chou reigns undertaken in his article listed above, Wai-kam Ho arrived at the conclusion that this *Li* belongs in the mid Western Chou period, about 950–900 B.C. according to Ch'en Meng-chia's chronology.

58 PAIR OF HU VESSELS
Later Western Chou
H. 24¾ in., W. 13 in.
Mr. and Mrs. Earl Morse, New York City

These monumental vessels, of flattened pear-shape, bulge above the molded feet, and taper toward the tall, straight necks. The lid of each vessel is surmounted by a ring like an inverted foot ring, on which the molding of the actual foot ring is repeated. The belly is decorated with heavy, rounded, relief figures on plain ground, set in panels formed by flat relief bands. These relief bands run horizontally and vertically, like a harness, crossing in the center of each of the four sides. Diamonds in high relief mark the crossings; above and below them are halved diamonds. There are eight panels in all, filled with disconnected and greatly distorted T'ao-t'ieh elements. At the lower part of the neck runs a band divided into four sections and filled with vaguely zoomorphous figures, each with an eye in the center of two loops. The upper part of the neck is bare. Similar zoomorphs, shaped like recumbent S-figures with an eye in the middle, appear on the lid. These figures are not arranged symmetrically, but in a continuous procession. Strong loop handles with movable disks are placed at the level of the neck band. Sculptured animal heads constructed of curvilinear forms adorn the handles. From their muzzles sally forth flattish, trunk-like, upcurved extensions with tiny, spurred flanges in front. The patina is gray-green.

Published: Fong Chow, *Animals and Birds in Chinese Art*, No. 9.

In their ponderous dignity, these heavy, tall vessels are impressive monuments. Their ornaments have become conventionalized to such a degree that it becomes difficult to recognize individual features. The same dissolved patterns, framed by the same bands with diamonds, occur in two vases of the same type with a few distinctive accessories. One of them, in the Brundage collection, is crowned by a lid with an openwork railing in the form of a wave pattern on top; its handles, with similar animal heads and upward extensions, show these extensions surmounted by small dragon heads with long, curved tusks (d'Argencé, *Brundage Bronzes*, pl. 35 A; *Sekai Kōkogaku Taikei*, VI, 1958, fig. 136). The other vessel has lost its lid; its animal handles have no extensions; its foot is decorated with a band of hanging "petals" or scales; and its inscription indicates that it originated in the state of Kuo, Northern Kuo, according to Kuo Mo-jo (*Liang Chou, K'ao-shih*, 246a: *Kuo Chi-shih Tzu-tsu Hu*; Jung Keng, *Shang Chou*, fig. 729; Karlgren, "Yin and Chou," C 83). This vessel is assigned to late Western Chou, while the Brundage *Hu* in d'Argencé's catalogue is dated to the 9th–8th c. B.C.

Late Western Chou

H. 24 in., DIAM. 14½ in.

Avery Brundage Collection, M. H. de Young Memorial Museum, San Francisco

A tall, round vessel with flaring foot has a tapering body, widest toward the bottom, two loops with suspended rings, and a lid. The decoration is arranged in three horizontal zones without vertical divisions. The same motif of broad, concave, undulating bands recurs in each zone. In the two lower zones these bands are doubled, and the spaces below and between their crests are filled with elements of slightly varied, geometric design. In the upper zone, the wave pattern is formed by a single band, and the space between the crests is left blank. A much smaller variant of the undulating band girds the lower zone of the lid; the spaces above and below the band are filled with kidney-shaped forms emitting three spikes, in alternating positions. This lower zone of the lid is surmounted by a short, inverted cone girdled by a fluted belt and topped by a flaring rim. Another narrow frieze adorns the foot, where we see a simple pattern of repeated, recumbent, S-shaped volutes formed by broad, grooved bands. Two sturdy loops emerge from the wall at the level of the dividing strip between the upper and the middle zone of the body; they are masked with modeled animal heads constructed with curvilinear elements, namely: circular eyes, upcurled muzzles, and convoluted, cone-shaped horns curving down around the eyes.

The lid bears an inscription of thirty characters plus two reduplicates, which I tentatively translate as follows:

> It was in the 26th year, the tenth moon, the first quarter, on the day *chi-mao*, [when] Fan Chü Sheng had this bridal *Hu* cast as a bridal gift for his first child, Meng Fei Kuai. May sons and grandsons forever treasure and use it!

Published: *Cheng-sung-t'ang*, ch. 7:32; *Hsiao-chiao*, ch. 4:92; Kuo Mo-jo, *Liang Chou*, 130 b, and *K'ao-shih*, 134 a; *Tsun-ku-chai*, Pt. I, ch. 2:30; Ferguson, *Li-tai chu-lu chi-chin-mu*, p. 224; Jung Keng, *Shang Chou*, Vol. I, p. 437, Vol. II, fig. 720; d'Argencé, *Brundage Bronzes*, pl. XXXIV B ("871 B.C.").

This stately vessel ranks among the comparatively rare instances of bronzes dated to a year in a Chou king's reign. The king's name, of course, is not mentioned. But since there were only a few late Western Chou kings with reigns recorded to have exceeded twenty years, the possible equations are limited to these few. A further limitation may be afforded by the ductus and the tenor of the inscriptions, as well as by the style of the ornaments of a bronze. In the present case, the 26th year was taken by Kuo Mo-jo to refer to the reign of Li Wang (878–842 B.C., according to the "orthodox" Chou chronology), thus corresponding with 853 B.C. On epigraphic evidence, however, as gathered by Ch'en Meng-chia, Li Wang reigned for only sixteen years, whereas his predecessor, I Wang, attained as many as thirty years. Hence this 26th year would refer to the reign of I Wang (894–879 B.C., in Liu Hsin's "orthodox" reckoning). The adoption of the reign years vouchsafed by existing inscriptions, however, requires us to abandon the conventional or orthodox chronology. It is replaced by a revised chronology based on the minimum reign years known from inscriptions, and also tailored to fit the wider framework supplied by the few hints in Chou literature at the duration of the early part, as well as at the whole, of Western Chou. I Wang's reign, in Ch'en Meng-chia's revised chronology, covered the years 887–858 B.C., approximately; his 26th year, therefore, would fall to about 862 B.C. The discrepancy between the two dates, 853 B.C. and 862 B.C., is insignificant indeed. We should not rule out the possibility, however, of a date in Hsüan Wang's reign (827–

782 B.C.), whose 26th year would correspond to 802 B.C.

Through the style of its décor the Brundage *Hu* is related to a group of bronzes whose inscriptions point to the same period: the bronzes made by *shan-fu* K'o, "seneschal K'o," whose grandfather had served under Kung Wang (946–935; in Ch'en's shortened chronology, about 927–908), and by a few contemporaries. To this group, listed by Karlgren under B87–97 in his "Yin and Chou in Chinese Bronzes," pp. 41–43, an important new find of 1942 made in ancient Chou territory in Shensi has to be added, an inscribed tripod, *Yü Ting* (see *KKHP*, XXV, 1959, and T. Higuchi, "A New Study on Western Chou Bronzes," p. 85 ff.). The decoration of the *Yü Ting* is similar to that of the *K'o Ting*; the main frieze is occupied by an undulating band of the same kind as the three bands of the Brundage *Hu*.

It remains to be mentioned that Fan Chü Sheng, the "maker" of the Brundage *Hu*, is believed to be identical with Fan Sheng, "maker" of the *Fan Sheng Kuei*, assigned to the reign of Li Wang by Kuo Mo-jo (*Liang Chou t'u-lu*, fig. 106: lid only; *K'ao-shih*, 133 a).

As for the date of this *Hu*, the fact that K'o's vessels were made two generations after Kung Wang appears to be decisive; by either manner of reckoning we arrive in the first half of the ninth or the middle of the ninth century at the latest for his vessels, so that the possible equations of the 26th year with 853 B.C. or ca. 862 B.C. in the inscription of the Brundage *Hu* fit in very well.

60   KUEI
Late Western Chou
H. 9 in., DIAM. (without handles) 9¼ in.
Mr. and Mrs. Myron S. Falk, Jr., New York City

This round jar with lid has a ring-foot supported by three short legs, which are joined to animal heads overlaid across the foot. Above the horizontally furrowed belly the wall recedes, slanting toward the rim. The lid forms a low dome capped by a flaring ring. Two small perforations at the base of this ring would allow the lid to be tied to the vessel. There are three bands of ornament: at the foot, diagonals with short hooks; at the slanting neck, a wider frieze with disconnected, grooved, relief bands, with oval eyes suggesting dissolved zoomorphous images; and a similar band circling the lid near the edge. Two short, sturdy, loop handles bearing loose rings are cast onto the neck; they are surmounted by animal heads with spiraling coils as horns, distinct from the flat-horned heads above the legs. The patina is brownish-green.

Published: J. D. La Plante, *Arts of the Chou Dynasty*, Stanford University Museum, 1958, No. 43.

The décor of this vessel, a type that seems to have replaced in the course of the Western Chou period the old *Kuei* with curved sides and large handles, as exemplified by the Peacock *Kuei* from Minneapolis, No. 49, is a classic sample of design in a phase that was nothing less than classic.

Fluting of the walls apparently was not fashionable in early Western Chou. A single fluted *Kuei* dated so early (Jung Keng, *Shan-chai t'u-lu*, 2:83; *Shang Chou*, fig. 307) opposes no less than twenty-six pieces ascribed to late Western Chou in Jung Keng's corpus (*Shang Chou*, figs. 310, 319–328, 330–344).

61   LEI
Early Eastern Chou
H. 10⅞ in., DIAM. 11¹³⁄₁₆ in.
Worcester Art Museum; gift of Mrs. F. Harold Daniels

A flat-bottomed vessel with a wide, convex shoulder has a narrow, straight neck, and broad, everted mouth rim. Two small loop handles are cast onto the shoulder at opposite sides. The decoration is done in broad, double-grooved bands in sharp-edged, low relief on plain ground, arranged in two registers. All of these grooved bands terminate in dragon heads at both ends. Organized in units of three dragons, in a configuration that is repeated in the next unit, the decoration forms a pattern that covers the surface evenly, without regard to a central axis or symmetry. Nor are the dragons that form each unit identical. One, longer than the rest, his heads in the lower left and upper right corners of the rectangle occupied by the unit, forms a long, S-shaped band that divides the unit vertically, the center being marked by a raised eye. A smaller dragon, distinguished by a crest in the form of yet another dragon head, fills the space to the right of the S-band, while the smallest dragon's heads look down from the upper left corner. Each of the long dragon's two heads has a raised eye; the smaller dragons possess only one such eye, in the larger of their heads. In the frieze of the lower half of the vessel, the configurations are exactly as in the upper frieze except that, to fit the given space, the dragon having a "dragon-head" crest is placed in the upper left corner. The two friezes are separated by a plain band of the same width as the dragon bodies. The neck is plain.

Published: Worcester Art Museum *News Bulletin and Calendar*, XXII/5, February, 1957, p. 27 (illustrated), and *Annual Report*, 1957, p. 13 (listed).

The type is not invariably called *Lei*. A common alternative is *P'ou*, but even *Hu* was used (Umehara, *Kodōki keitai*, pl. 19). The shape of the vessel agrees with the older *Lei* (No. 42) rather than with the *P'ou* (Nos. 15, 18, 19). In fact this type is named *Lei* in an inscription of a similar vessel of somewhat later date, recently found in Shantung (cf. *KKHP*, XXXII, 1963/2, pp. 59–64).

As regards the date of the Worcester *Lei*, its ornamentation suggests a period as early as the 8th c. B.C., as it closely resembles the dragon patterns of bronze objects excavated at Hsin-ts'un in Hsün-hsien, Honan, from tombs assigned to the reigns of Yu Wang (781–771) and P'ing Wang (770–720), that is, end of Western Chou to early Eastern Chou (*Hsün-hsien Hsin-ts'un Report*, pls. 73, 74). The shape of the vessel is almost duplicated in a plain *Lei* among excavation finds of 1954–55 from Lo-yang, datable Eastern Chou II or 7th c. B.C. (*Lo-yang Chung-chou-lu*, pl. 52:2). While a date as late as 7th c. should therefore be taken into consideration,

the fact that the vessel originates from Shensi, the territory given up by the Chou in 771 B.C., supports an earlier date, one toward the end of Western Chou.

A very similar piece in the National Central Museum was published by T'an Tan-ch'iung (*Decorative Patterns*, No. 66, pl. 26) as a Ch'un-ch'iu (8th to 6th c.) example. Stylistically later vessels of this type show a denser and more regular arrangement of the dragons; they are all in the same position and their size decreases, while the number of the zones accordingly increases. The individual dragon figures, therefore, become submerged in patterns (e.g., *Senoku Seishō*, rev. ed., No. 74, pl. 19). In a still later phase the dragons are linked to one another in endless chains running lengthwise and further interlaced by bands running crosswise (e.g., *Pillsbury Collection*, No. 52). The time intervals at stake are probably rather brief ones; the Pillsbury *Lei* may possibly date from the late 8th century B.C.

62 TUI
Early Eastern Chou
H. 4¾ in., W. 5½ in.
Stanford University Museum; gift of Mortimer C. Leventritt

This semiglobular bowl, on a concave foot with splayed, molded base, has two tubular loop handles at opposite sides. The cover has sloping sides and a flattened, convex top with a small, upright ring in the center. Near the edge of the cover stand three half-figures of long-necked birds, which function as legs when the cover is inverted. The decoration of the bowl consists of two rows of oblong panels showing a slightly recessed, presumably stamped "Hsin-cheng pattern" in low and slightly blurred relief. The panels are separated by vertical and horizontal plain strips, and framed by a rope sling pattern overlying the plain strips. Where the vertical strands of the rope cross the rope running along the middle, they are tied into knots. On the cover the same design is repeated in two concentric zones. There is a smooth, gray-green patina.

Published: La Plante, *Arts of the Chou Dynasty*, No. 57.

The assumed provenance from Hsin-cheng, Honan, though arguable on stylistic grounds, cannot be considered as certain. The type is not recorded among the Hsin-cheng finds. It is encountered, however, among the vessels of the hoard from Li-yü, Shansi, in the ancient Chin (Tsin) territory (see Shang Ch'eng-tsu, *Hun-yüan i-ch'i-t'u*, Nanking, 1936, pl. 10), where it occurs also in tripod form (*ibid.*, pls. 5, 6). Both the tripod and a ring-footed vessel are now kept in the Shanghai Museum (*Shanghai Museum Bronzes*, pls. 69, 70), with other bronzes from the same hoard (*ibid.*, pls. 68, 71–74). The tripod and the *Tui* are decorated with inlaid copper dragon patterns and tiger figures of typical Li-yü style (not visible in the *Hun-yüan* reproductions), but the "Hsin-cheng pattern" and the rope sling are perfectly represented in a squat *Ting* (*Shanghai Museum Bronzes*, pl. 68; *Hun-yüan*, pls. 3, 4, 19, 22), as is the scheme of oblong panels in concentric zones on the lid of a *Hu* with ropes tied around its body

(*Hun-yüan*, pl. 19). While these analogies do not at all imply that the Stanford piece originated in Li-yü, they do tie it to the Hsin-cheng types within the Li-yü hoard, thus suggesting a date about middle Ch'un-ch'iu, say around 600 B.C.

A more recently excavated group of tombs at Chia-ko-chuang, T'ang-shan, Hopei, in an area that belonged to the ancient state of Yen, yielded another and even more similar *Tui* (*Archaeology in New China*, pl. 57:1). The finds were estimated to date from the beginning of the Warring States, about 500 B.C. (*KKHP*, VI, 1953; Watson, *Archaeology in China*, p. 27f.; Chêng Tê-k'un, *Chou China*, 124f., dates the finds too late), but in *Lo-yang Chung-chou-lu*, p. 130, in a brief critical survey of important sites, similarities with Hsin-cheng are noted and an earlier date suggested, namely, 6th–5th c. B.C. As a consequence, the Stanford bronze may safely be taken to date from the sixth century at the latest.

63   COVERED TING

Early Eastern Chou
H. 10¹¹⁄₁₆ in., DIAM. 11 in.
Royal Ontario Museum, Toronto

A tripod with a deep cauldron is covered by a domed lid whose flattened top is surmounted by a strongly flaring rim. The legs are curved, bulging at the top and splayed toward the bottom. The handles are shaped as rectangular loops and bent outward, reversing the curve of the convex wall from which they spring. The decoration consists of continuous patterns of interlaced bands in separated friezes. The frieze under the rim is widest. It is filled with interlaced bands of non-zoomorphous character, in four tiers. These bands, quite distinct from those on the *Lei*, No. 61, are divided into a plain strip and a meander strip. In the upper half, the plain strips lie on top; in the lower half they lie at the bottom of the bands. But, entering the adjoining unit, the bands from the lower half of the previous unit move into the upper half, and in doing so they twist. Thus, there is interlacing and twisting as well as reversal, as the bands in the lower half of the frieze move in the opposite direction. In each unit the plain bands at top and bottom end in a curl, in front of which there is a disconnected, plain element like an angular spiral, accompanied on one side by a band of slanting striae. Below a strong, molded "rope," which encircles the vessel below the main frieze, there is a narrow zone in which the design of the lower half of the main frieze is repeated. On the lid are concentric friezes showing complicated variants of the design described. Below the narrow frieze on the belly is a wreath of hanging petals filled with symmetrical figures of curls.

Not previously published.

The style of the décor is none too familiar. It has no name, and its chronological position has yet to be worked out. Provisionally we might speak of a proto-Li-yü style, for there are obvious affinities with Li-yü designs for which a later date is certain. Interesting is the fact that this vessel's artistic merits are surpassed by its technical excellence. There is a curious vagueness about the ornaments, especially those on the lid, suggesting a state of experimentation. There are also reminiscences of Hsin-cheng: the flaring ring on the lid, the molded rope around the belly, the hanging petals, the system of interlacery, and the oblique striae.

The pattern of the main frieze is almost the same as that of a mold fragment from the Hou-ma site in S. W. Shansi (*Archaeology in New China*, pl. 52, top), a site identified as that of the last capital of the Chin state. The move to this "New Field," Hsin-t'ien, as the new capital was named, was made under Duke Ching toward the middle of March, 584 B.C. (cf. A. Tschepe, S.J., *Histoire du Royaume de Tsin*, Shanghai, 1910, p. 178 f.; *Shih-chi*, ch. 14, ed. Ku Chieh-kang, 1936, I, 328, under 583 B.C.). Several foundries were discovered during the excavations begun in 1957. Some of these made only coins, others made belt hooks, still others specialized in ritual vessels. This specialization and the enormous quantity of mold fragments found (about 30,000) testify to the importance of the local bronze industry, whose fortunes declined, however, after the middle of the 5th c. B.C. (cf. *Wen Wu*, 1960/8–9, 1961/10; *Kaogu*, 1962/2, 1963/5; Chêng Tê-k'un

Chou China, 26ff., 70ff.). Bronzes decorated in the style represented by the pottery molds were actually found in tombs of the Ch'un-ch'iu period excavated at the Hou-ma-chen site (Chêng Tê-k'un, *op. cit.*, p. 71). The likely date of the mold fragment mentioned above is the 6th c. B.C.

The sixth-century date is confirmed by a coeval *Ting* found in an Eastern Chou III (6th c.) tomb at Lo-yang (*Lo-yang Chung-chou-lu*, pl. 58:1), a *Ting* of rather more advanced style. A *Ting* said to have been excavated in Hui-hsien, assigned to the 5th c. by Watson (*Ancient Chinese Bronzes*, pl. 61a; rubbing of the décor in *Shan-piao-chen yü Liu-li-ko*, pl. 77:2, showing a typical Hsin-cheng pattern on the handle, pl. 77:1), stands about midway between the Toronto vessel and the Lo-yang *Ting*. Sharing as it does the décor of the main frieze of the Toronto *Ting*, and the three small upright rings replacing the heavy inverted ring-foot on the lid of the Lo-yang vessel, it doubtless dates about a century farther back in time than was estimated by Watson.

The fact that a sixth-century date of the ornament style of No. 63 is ascertainable does not rule out the possibility of earlier beginnings, for the style is rooted in seventh century conventions; nor does it imply that similar patterns did not survive into the fifth century. A rare combination of this proto-Li-yü style with the fully developed Li-yü style in the décor of a single *Ting* in the Trautmann collection is a case in point (see G. Ecke, *Sammlung Trautmann*, No. 19).

64 TING

Eastern Chou, Late Ch'un-ch'iu
H. 9¼ in., DIAM. 10½ in.
Mr. and Mrs. Frederick M. Mayer, New York City

The short legs of this tripod fuse with the body's rounded contours; it is covered with a convex lid. At opposite sides of the vessel, mask-and-ring handles are attached at the level of the upper frieze. Three recumbent animals, each of which holds a movable ring in its mouth, are placed on the lid, in a circle bordering the lower frieze. Except for its bottom and feet, the entire surface of the *Ting* is decorated. Plain, horizontal bands divide the décor into superposed friezes. The dividing band encircling the body at its widest part is accentuated by a ridge decorated with finely incised cowrie shells. The patterns within the friezes are unrelated to such structural divisions as are offered by the legs, the handles, or the animals on the lid. Vertical divisions and symmetry are avoided. The patterns consist of interlocked bands in evenly flat relief, with overlapping, curved ends turning at right angles, and with rounded corners. Lined on both sides by smooth strips, these bands are embellished with fine, small spirals, S-spirals, slanting striations, scales, and some granulated areas. In the main frieze, the bands issue to both sides from "ox-heads" or "bucrania" in alternatingly inverted positions. In the narrower zones the "bucrania" are missing. A particular, if secondary, feature is the presence of plain "fillers" occupying the empty spaces between the figures from which they take their shapes. There is a smooth, variegated green patina.

Not previously published.

Compared with typical *Ting* tripods of the Shang period (e.g., Nos. 20, 22), where bowl and legs are distinct members of a composite structure, the shape of the present type is compact and completely unified. It would be difficult to decide where, in this integrated structure, the legs begin; they simply have become elements of a whole. Presumably it is because of the fusion of legs and body that this type is sometimes called *Li-Ting*. This designation, however, refers to tripods with a trilobate body like that of a *Li* and with solid legs like those of a *Ting*, and therefore does not apply here.

A very similar piece was in the collection of Dr. Otto Burchard, a piece that differed in only one respect: it had a ring handle attached to the center of the lid. Judging from the reproduction in L. Reidemeister's catalogue (*Die Bestände der Firma Dr. Otto Burchard & Co.*, 1935, No. 291, pl. 30), it has the same "fillers" as described above, but the grooves surrounding them appear as black lines, and their blackness is due, no doubt, to some kind of inlay. This black inlay, reminiscent of a technique practised in Shang times (Nos. 19, 20, 22, 23, 26), can be seen also on the sixth century *Ting* from Toronto (No. 63), as well as on a very large *Ting* of Li-yü II style in the Brundage collection (cf. d'Argencé, *Brundage Bronzes*, pl. 39), about contemporary with the Mayer *Ting*, No. 64. In the Brundage *Ting* the black areas are more conspicuous because they are not reduced to grooves by the "fillers" such as we observe in the Burchard and Mayer pieces. The question arises whether the "fillers" were introduced to eliminate the large, empty interstices—with the effect of a denser pattern, or whether, on the contrary, the "fillers" were removed to emphasize the interstices—with the effect of greater clarity of the pattern. An answer may be supplied by a consideration of the technical requirements in either case. When the model of the vessel to be cast is made, the fillers, forming part of the model surface, are there as a matter of course; they come into being as soon as grooves are cut along the positive pattern of the bands surrounding them. It takes a further effort to clear these surface remnants out and level the negative spaces evenly. Con-

sequently it would seem that the fillers were not introduced for the effect of density, as an element of style, but simply represent a technically less laborious procedure and are without any stylistic significance.

A fine example of a model fragment of the same style from the Hou-ma-chen site in Shansi, reproduced with several mold fragments in *Wen Wu*, 1960/8–9, p. 9, fig. 9, shows a bucranium with bigger horns amid meandered bands on countersunk ground, clear of fillers; its archaeological context permits a date between 584 and about 450 B.C. (see commentary under No. 63 above), while its style suggests a date in the late sixth century, perhaps as late as toward 500. A similar pattern, but with "fillers," occurs on a *Chien* excavated at Fen-shui-ling in Shansi from an early Warring States tomb (*KKHP*, XV, 1957/1, p. 110, fig. 3; cf. *Kaogu*, 1964/3, 111–137, pls. 1–7; Watson, *Ancient Chinese Bronzes*, p. 59), again suggesting a date around 500 or not long afterward.

The style of this *Ting* is characterized by the motif of interlocked bands with their fine, filling ornament, by the flat relief, and by overlapping parts, creating the illusion of layers. It is the style referred to above as Li-yü II. An exemplary instance of this style is offered by a *Ting* formerly in the Holmes collection (Umehara, *Sengoku*, pls. 30–33).

Li-yü I, not represented among the exhibits, is the style of the simpler, interlocked, dragon bands with filling ornaments but without overlapping parts (*Sengoku*, pls. 1, 2, 7, 10; *Freer Gallery Bronzes*, pl. 31; *Buckingham Bronzes*, pl. 51). If Li-yü II on archaeological grounds is datable around 500 B.C., Li-yü I cannot but be placed in the latter half of the sixth century, say about 525 B.C., while its forerunners or proto-Li-yü styles (e.g., No. 63 above; or *Sengoku*, pls. 34, 38, 124) may stretch back as far as about 600 B.C.

Li-yü III, presupposing the designs of Li-yü II, adds layered relief. Two outstanding examples of this style which are datable through their inscriptions give a secure chronological support to the entire Li-yü style sequence. One is the *Chih Chün Tzu Chien* in the Freer Gallery, datable *before* 453 B.C. (*Freer Gallery Bronzes*, pl. 30); the other one is a pair of *Hu* in the Cull collection, datable 482 B.C. or soon after

(W. P. Yetts, *The Cull Chinese Bronzes*, pls. 16, 17). Both of them appear to have originated in the state of Chin (Tsin) or modern Shansi, the same province where Li-yü is located.

The fact that the *Huang-ch'ih Hu* pair dates from 482 B.C. would seem to establish the entire sequence as a late Ch'un-ch'iu creation, just preceding the Warring States period.

65   PIEN-HU
Late Eastern Chou
H. 10⁹⁄₁₆ in., w. 10 in.
Kunstindustrimuseum, Copenhagen

An oval bottle or canteen with flat sides, low, cylindrical neck, and flaring mouth stands on a rectangular, molded foot. On the shoulders, small, relief masks with loop muzzles hold movable suspension rings decorated with inlay work. Rows of inlaid copper triangles encircle both neck and foot. The sides are decorated with an exquisitely designed, stamped pattern of small feather-curls in layered relief, arranged like brick masonry and separated by a trellis of plain bands.

Published: Det danske Kunstindustrimuseum, *Virksomhed* 1959–64, p. 97 f.

This appealing type, a secular rather than ritual bronze vessel, seems to have made its appearance no earlier than the 5th-4th centuries and to have lasted into Han times. The existing examples reveal little variation. Possibly the earlier forms had a more rounded silhouette than the later ones. A specimen in the Pillsbury Collection (Karlgren, *Pillsbury Collection*, No. 56) may, on account of the peculiar, architectonically unsolved design of the lowermost tier and foot, precede most of the specimens.

Comparable vessels in addition to the Pillsbury example are in the following collections: Verburgt (Visser, *Asiatic Art*, 1948, pl. 24); Pilster (*International Exhibition of Chinese Art*, London, 1935–36, No. 142, *Commemorative Catalogue*, pl. 31); *Wu-ying-tien*, 122 (also London Exhibition, No. 83); The Mount Trust (Watson, *Ancient Chinese Bronzes*, pl. 67 b); J. T. Tai (Chêng Tê-k'un, *Chou China*, pl. 24a); Art Institute of Chicago (*Buckingham Bronzes*, pl. 57); Tenri Sankōkan (Mizuno, *Bronzes and Jades*, pl. 147).

66 TUMBLER
Late Eastern Chou
H. 15⅝ in., DIAM. 6¾ in.
Dr. Paul Singer, Summit, New Jersey

A tall, plain, tumbler-like vase with tapering body and slightly expanded low foot, is covered with a low-domed lid. On the lid stand four upright rings in radial position. On the body two rings are held by small, looped animal masks in very low relief, brazed to the wall. The surface is covered by yellowish green patina and azurite patches; in the interior are large areas coated by azurite.
    Published: Loehr, *Relics*, No. 69a, color plate p. 67.

The patination is very like that of bronzes from Shou-chou, Anhui, of the Warring States period. The elegant shape of this vessel seems to be without pedigree, even though it may call to mind the artless elegance of the smaller tumbler of hoary age from Oxford (No. 1).
    The only comparable bronze of this shape known to the author, reproduced in Mizuno's *Bronzes and Jades*, pl. 148, is in an unnamed collection. The rings on the lid of that bronze are adorned with scaly dragon figures in the round, and in addition to the ring masks, which are in high relief and seem to represent archaizing versions of buffalo heads, there is a small loop handle with another archaistic bovine head near the foot, similar in position and function to the lower handle of the *Lei* from the Metropolitan Museum, No. 42.

67　TUI-TING
Late Eastern Chou
H. 6¾ in., w. (including handles) 7¼ in.
Ashmolean Museum, Oxford

The two halves of this round vessel with a cover of equal shape and height form a flattened sphere. The bowl stands on three short legs topped by animal masks in relief, while the cover is provided with a low stand-ring instead. The only sculptural element in the décor of the surfaces is a "rope" that separates each half into two zones. The zones are filled with sunken, simple, linear figures arranged in endless patterns. A small plait pattern runs around the stand-ring on top. Circular handles are attached to the sides, near the rims of both vessel and lid. The surface is covered by a smooth, light green patina.

Published: Watson, *Ancient Chinese Bronzes*, pl. 66a.

A vessel of the same type and size, apparently with the same decoration, is in the Pillsbury collection, Minneapolis Institute of Arts (Karlgren, *Pillsbury Collection*, No. 49).

The Eastern Chou globular vessels are named *Tui*, a term also applied by Jung Keng to tripods with more or less globular, lidded bowls. Karlgren prefers the designation *Ting*. But "Tui" fails to denote the fact that this type is a tripod, much as "Ting" fails to evoke its specific form. On the analogy of *Li-Ting*, the term *Tui-Ting* would seem in order.

The date proposed by Watson, "late 5th-4th c. B.C.," seems acceptable but requires archaeological support that is now wanting.

68   TUI
Late Eastern Chou
H. 6¾ in., DIAM. 5½ in.
Mr. and Mrs. Frederick M. Mayer, New York City

This is a rare type of round vessel which, together with its cover, is of perfectly ovoid shape. A circular knob on the cover corresponds to its small, splayed, flat foot but is smaller in diameter. The body is encircled at even intervals by fluted, plain bands. Between these bands lie convex, slightly swelling zones which are decorated. The design of the bottom zone is repeated on the upper zones of both body and lid; the pattern on the central zone of the body is repeated on the lower zone of the lid. The motifs are geometric and very unobtrusively handled, in sunken lineament. At the bottom is a band of triangles with alternating fillings; above it, a band of oblongs with crossed diagonals; in the third zone we find the triangles again; and on the lid, first the rectangles with diagonals, and finally once more the triangles. At the level of the topmost zone of décor on the body, the vessel has two circular, loop handles. Green patina covers the outside; in the interior, there is much deep blue azurite.

Not previously published.

While I am unable to mention a counterpart to this vessel, which is remarkable for its restrained elegance, I wish to refer to a *Tui* of bronze excavated from an early Warring States tomb at Fen-shui-ling in Ch'ang-chih, Shansi (*Kaogu*, XCI, 1964/3, pl. 3:3). Apparently the top and bottom halves of that specimen are of equal size, and both halves are fitted with ring loops, like the Oxford *Tui-Ting*, No. 67. On the whole, the *Tui* constructed of equal halves appear to be later than those where the body is larger than the lid. If, on that ground, an earlier date than is warranted by the Fen-shui-ling evidence (roughly, early 5th c. B.C.) should be considered, it ought to be supported by the décor style. The décor of No. 68 does not offer this kind of support, I believe.

An egg-shaped, small tripod with fluted body and cover which is fitted with upright rings instead of the circular knob, a *Tui-Ting* in the Brundage collection, compares with regard to the shape and proportions of body and lid (Consten, *Das alte China*, pl. 47).

The *Tui* occurs also in lacquer, and the bronze No. 68, while probably earlier, compares very well with a beautiful lacquer box in the Nelson-Atkins Gallery in Kansas City, of ovoid shape and formed of two equal halves, mounted with gilt bronze rings at the rims and with annular feet (*ibidem*, color pl. iv).

69 FANG-HU
Late Eastern Chou
H. 18½ in., w. 9¼ in.
Albright-Knox Art Gallery, Buffalo

A square vase with strongly curved walls and a lid in the shape of a truncated pyramid is supported by a slightly tapering foot. Animal masks in relief, holding movable, strong rings, appear on two sides, below the neck. The bulging sides are decorated with a geometric pattern of diagonally crossed bands enclosing lozenges, in the center of which sit shiny, gold bosses. The bands are filled with zigzag lines crossing each other; these lines, alternately thick and thin, are enlivened by small curls and appendages. The ground, now bare, may have held some inlay when the vessel was new. Within the lozenges no ground is visible; apparently the sunken parts of the geometric ornaments were inlaid with a metallic substance such as niello. Above the ring-masks, where the neck begins, a horizontal band separates the zone of the neck from that of the belly. A wide zigzag band, with a filling of geometric figures similar to those in the bands below, moves around the neck. The triangles above and below this zigzag band hold gold bosses like those in the lozenges. On the sloping planes of the lid are four animal figures in the round, whose bodies coalesce with small upright rings. The patina is a grayish green.

Not previously published.

This superb vessel once belonged to a pair, its counterpart being known through exhibitions held in 1940 (The Detroit Institute of Arts: *Ancient Chinese Ritual Bronzes*, No. 73, pl. 32) and 1958 (La Plante, *Arts of the Chou Dynasty*, No. 65, lent by Frank Caro).

In three ways the décor of this *Hu* indicates a break with older traditions: the zoomorphic motifs are abandoned and replaced by geometric figures of recent vintage; relief effects are avoided; and color enters, in the form of inlays and gold. The masks holding the rings are as conventional as the figures on the cover; they do not contradict the fact that geometric designs dominate.

A round *Hu* from Chin-ts'un, Lo-yang, published by Mizuno (*Bronzes and Jades*, color pl. 12) demonstrates the role of color more strikingly. This vessel is inlaid with gold, silver, and blue and white glass paste. While its décor is arranged in zones, the particular features of the diagonally crossed bands and the gold bosses—here placed atop the crossings—are present. This dazzling, round *Hu* is likely to be somewhat earlier than the square one from Buffalo, but unfortunately it is not closely datable: Mizuno's suggested date spans the 300 years from 500 to 200 B.C. If the latest tombs at Chin-ts'un are unlikely to be later than the end of the Han principality in 230 B.C., however, as maintained by Karlgren ("Notes on a Kin-ts'un Album," 74–81), the lower limit has to be raised accordingly. Moreover, since vessels of this kind are apt to have been treasured possessions of their last owners or, perhaps, of their forbears, we should allow one or two generations before the time of the burial as the more likely *terminus post quem non*, that is, about 260 or 290 B.C., for the actual manufacture at the latest. Thus, the more probable time range to consider would be narrowed to about 500–300 B.C.

More important than speculating on the absolute date by dead reckoning, however, because ultimately more precise, is the understanding of the relative position of a vessel within a group or sequence of which it forms part. As it is not possible here to undertake an investigation that would require much space, the sequence I conceive of is presented without further ado:

1. Round *Hu* (Mizuno, *Bronzes and Jades*, pl. 12) described above: straight diagonal bands crossing.

2. Buffalo *Fang-Hu*, No. 69, described above: straight diagonals crossing in a simple pattern.

3. *Fang-Hu*, Mrs. Eugene Meyer collection, Washington (Umehara, *Seika*, III, 214; *idem*, *Sengoku*, pl. 46:2; Jung Keng, *Shang Chou*, fig. 777): still straight diagonals, but enriched by "talons" and with a resultant emphasis on the central axis; simple zigzags on the foot.

4. *Pien-Hu*, Freer Gallery of Art (Umehara, *Seika*, III, 219; Mizuno, *Bronzes and Jades*, pl. 146): broken or deflected diagonals, not crossing the central axis, and continually changing in width.

5. Globular *Tui*, Fogg Art Museum, Winthrop collection (Umehara, *Sengoku*, pl. 46:1): deflected diagonals of involved design on a spherical surface and therefore difficult to evaluate in comparison with the preceding design.

6. *Fang-Hu*, University of Pennsylvania Museum (Umehara, *Seika*, III, 213; *Sengoku*, pl. 95:1; Jung Keng, *Shang Chou*, fig. 774; fine reproduction in Andersson's "The Goldsmith in Ancient China," pls. 19, 20): extremely involved design that is hard to read on account of inlay, apparently still based on crossing, though deflected, diagonals with stress on axis; a decoration of stupendous richness. Clear and relatively simple zigzags on the foot. Inscription, incised, is dated to "the King's fifth year," which probably refers to Hsiang Wang of Ch'i, whose fifth regnal year corresponds to 279 B.C. (cf. Kuo Mo-jo, *Liang Chou, K'ao-shih*, 220b; *Shih-chi*, ch. 15, ed. Ku Chieh-kang, 1936, Vol. I, p. 215; Karlgren, "Notes on a Kin-ts'un Album," p. 78). Exhibited at China House, New York, 1962; see Bunker, *The Art of Eastern Chou*, No. 51.

7. *Fang-Hu* from Chin-ts'un (White, *Tombs of Old Lo-yang*, pl. 109; Umehara, *Sengoku*, pl. 95:2; *idem*, *Rakuyō Kinson*, pl. 16 of rev. ed.): virtually indistinguishable from the Philadelphia *Hu*.

8. Minneapolis *Fang-Hu*, No. 70 in this exhibition.

In this series, the Philadelphia *Fang-Hu* (No. 6) is the only datable item. A fourth century date is required, at least, for the stylistically earlier pieces. The Buffalo specimen, No. 69, close to the beginning of the sequence, may have to be placed in the early 4th, possibly in the 5th century B.C.

70　FANG-HU
Late Eastern Chou
H. 14⅛ in., w. 8⅛ in.
The Minneapolis Institute of Arts; bequest of Alfred F. Pillsbury

The square vase, with strongly curved walls rising from a straight, square foot, has two movable ring handles suspended from masks below the neck. The décor of the sides is bordered by smooth strips at the mouth and down the edges, and the lower part of the belly is left bare. Similarly framed panels on the foot are filled with symmetrical designs of curved, diagonal lines ending in volutes and swirls, flanking a tiny, quasi-floral stalk. Variants of these designs appear in the narrow bands which separate the three panels of ornament covering the sides of the vessel. The panels show intricately composed patterns of diagonally slanting bands of varying width, zigzagging and crossing each other but staying clear of the vertical axis, where these bands join to form a series of pendants or small stalks of quasi-floral character. The patterns stand out in low relief on a smooth ground that may have been covered with inlays of some kind. The patina is silvery green.

Published: Karlgren, *Pillsbury Collection*, No. 54, pl. 74, detail of mask, pl. 77 top; *Sekai Kōkogaku Taikei*, VI, 1958, fig. 235.

If, in the maze of lines and curls in these complex patterns, there appears unobtrusively, almost accidentally, a formation resembling or made to resemble a dragon head here and there, it does not alter the basically geometric nature of the design. The purely geometric basis of this design is clearly seen in the ornamentation of the beautiful, flat bottle with silver inlay of the Freer Gallery (No. 4 in the series outlined in the preceding entry, No. 69). The notion of "corrupted, dissolved, and geometricized" animals being the basis of the patterns, set forth in the catalogue of the collection, is as unacceptable as the interpretation of some of the small "floral" pendants down the median line as "playful corruptions" of the T'ao-t'ieh motif.

As regards the chronological position of this elegant vessel, the first question to ask is whether it is earlier or later than the Philadelphia *Fang-Hu* (No. 6 in the series found under No. 69 above). It seems to me that the pattern of No. 70 avoids the sharp angles in the ornaments of the other vessel; in No. 70, the angles are blunted or rounded off throughout, and the formation of the crossed diagonals on the foot in curves with curlicue ends, in particular, seems to demand a later date for the Minneapolis vessel, perhaps around 300 B.C.

71   FANG-HU
      Late Eastern Chou or Western Han
      H. 19¾ in., w. 10½ in.
      Victoria & Albert Museum, London

A tall, square vase on a slightly tapering foot has curved sides which, narrowing toward the neck, again widen a little toward a lip that is strengthened by a simple molding. Two movable ring handles are suspended from looped relief masks below the neck. As in the case of the Pillsbury vessel, No. 70, the decorative design covering the sides is framed by plain border strips, and the lower part of the side is left bare, save for three broad, hanging, pointed petals extending from the base of the decorated field. The magnificently designed décor is done in gold and silver inlay flush with the rest of the surface. It is composed of curvilinear scrolls of continually varying widths or sudden enlargements and contractions, which impart a sense of swiftness and suppleness to the scroll work. Arranged symmetrically at both sides of a median line emphasized by rather few but large elements, the composition, though entirely free of angular and straight forms, does recall the general layout of the decoration of No. 70 and the related earlier pieces listed under No. 69. Conceivably the masterful design of the Victoria & Albert Museum vessel represents a new, much advanced version within the same tradition, with curves taking the place of the older, sharply angular motifs. The ornaments on the foot, too, are doubtless derived from the crossing diagonals such as seen in No. 70, and the stalk with a concentric circle in the middle is certainly reminiscent of the concentric circles placed along the median line of that vessel. Free of corrosions, its bronze surface having acquired a deep brownish black tone, this extraordinary piece gives the impression of never having been exposed to the process of oxidation that takes place under ground. While offering a perfect foil for its dazzling inlay, the bronze looks startlingly different from recently excavated ones.

Published: R. Fry, L. Binyon, et al., *Chinese Art*, 1935, pl. 38; W. Watson, "Sung Bronzes," *TOCS*, 1959–60, pp. 33–38, pl. 85; R. S. Jenyns & W. Watson, *Chinese Art*, Vol. II: *The Minor Arts; Gold, Silver, Bronze, etc.*, pp. 86, 98, pl. 39.

In a short critique of this vessel in the book by Jenyns and Watson (pp. 86 and 98), Watson arrives at the verdict that this vessel "for all its fidelity to the inlay style of the late Chou period . . . is really a free invention in the terms of the ancient convention" by a master craftsman of the Sung period, and assigns it a date as late as A.D. 11th-12th c. His judgment is based on the formal properties such as the shape and some details of the ornamentation. While it may be perfectly true that an unquestionably ancient *Hu* with exactly the same ornamentation is not known today, the fact remains that in various aspects this vessel does closely resemble—in both shape and ornament—antique objects. If this bronze should indeed be a Sung creation, it may have to be rated a replica rather than a free invention. We must not overlook the fact that compared with typical Sung products (e.g., *op. cit.*, pls. 42, 43) it plainly appears to be ancient. If this magnificent vessel, therefore, should prove to be a Sung copy, it may yet faithfully represent a lost antique design. It is entirely free of the absurdities and inelegance of the common Sung and later imitations of ancient types.

72 HU WITH COVER

Late Eastern Chou
H. 5¾ in., DIAM. 3½ in.
The Art Institute of Chicago

This small, pear-shaped vessel on a molded ring-foot has a slightly convex, collared lid fitted inside the lip, with three conventional bird figures in the round on top. The body is decorated in three registers which are separated, and bordered, by plain bands overlaid with gold. The band circling the body at its widest part is accentuated by a slender roll in relief. Comparatively large-scale, broad, energetically curving scrolls inlaid in silver, contrasting with the dark tone of the bronze, swirl in the three friezes. The silver bands are bordered by thin, silver lines, which every now and then veer off to form fine, small spirals of their own. The design of the scrolls varies through their course as well as with the registers.

Published: Kelley and Ch'en, *Buckingham Bronzes*, pl. 58; Umehara, *Rakuyō Kinson*, rev. ed., 1944, pl. 23:1 (showing the state before cleaning); Bachhofer, *A Short History*, p. 49, fig. 39; Mizuno, *Bronzes and Jades*, pl. 141.

The first description given of the stylistic shift in late Eastern Chou geometric patterns is found in Bachhofer's *Short History*, p. 48 f., where we find also the observation that the inlay, so called, of this small *Hu* actually was hammered on. The technique was noticed by Karlgren in his description of the similar *Hu* now in the Sackler Collections, with details that will be mentioned under No. 73 below.

73   HU
Late Eastern Chou
H. 4¾ in., DIAM. 3⅛ in.
The Sackler Collections, New York City

Another small, pear-shaped vessel is of the same type as No. 72. The lid is missing. On the middle frieze small ring-holder masks are attached, which interfere with the scroll work in such a way that it must seem doubtful whether they were designed for this vessel. Throughout the design, which varies with the three registers, the scrolls appear to be constructed with volutes alternatingly turning clockwise and anti-clockwise. Unlike those of the Chicago *Hu*, the scroll bands are not invariably bordered by thin lines. Here, these thin lines appear to be confined to the inside of the curves. Again unlike the Chicago *Hu*, the volutes in the middle zone are terminated by bird-heads. "Rich deep-brown, often reddish, patina, with green patches."

    Published: Karlgren, "Notes on a Kin-ts'un Album," pls. 1, 4, pp. 68, 69 (whence the description of the patina); Detroit Institute of Arts: *An Exhibition of Ancient Chinese Ritual Bronzes*, No. 48, pl. 31; Umehara, *Rakuyō Kinson*, rev. ed., 1944, pl. 23:2; La Plante, *Arts of the Chou Dynasty*, No. 61.

An interesting observation concerning the "inlay" technique in Karlgren's paper of 1938 may be quoted here: "The silver has been laid on in threads, which have been flattened out, when hammered into the shallow depressions, so as to become strips about 0.1 cm. broad. The long loops are formed by from one up to seven parallel strips. These have been hammered so tightly together that in the best preserved places they give an impression of being sheets of silver." (*Op. cit.*, p. 69.)

74 TUI OR KUEI
End of Eastern Chou
H. 6 in., W. (including handles) 11⅞₆ in.
Musée Guimet, Paris

A round bowl on a simple foot-ring is covered with a lid whose contour continues that of the convex wall. Flat on top, the lid is surmounted by four bird figures whose bodies form upright rings, while their long necks and heads serve as feet when the lid is turned over. Two loop handles of surprisingly antique appearance are attached to the sides; they are masked by animal heads with shield-like upright horns above bird bodies, and are provided with rectangular appendages like those of the early Western Chou *Kuei* No. 48. The decoration consists of boldly designed bands. These are dynamic, and wholly asymmetrically placed, curved bands with curly edges and occasional spiky excrescences. The bands, which are inlaid in silver, are lined on both sides with thin silver lines that send forth, or terminate in, small, tightly coiled spirals, very similar to those scattered between the big spirals of the two *Hu*, Nos. 72 and 73. In the center of the lid, on a flat, circular, slightly raised patform, the ornaments circle and swirl about a small quatrefoil: the only instance of a clear, tectonic relationship of the ornament to the body of the vessel.

Published: Umehara, *Rakuyō Kinson*, rev. ed., 1944, p. 23, pl. 24 (including top view of the lid); *idem, Nihon Seika*, V, 369 (formerly S. Kawai, Kyoto).

This vessel, later than the small *Hu* bottles described under 72 and 73, hardly earlier than the late 3rd c. B.C., is remarkable for two reasons. One is the unprecedented degree of asymmetry of the ornament and the complete disregard, on the part of the designer, of anything like an architectonic order in the relation between his ornamentation and the structure of the vessel. The other reason is the unconcealed archaism in the guise of the bluntly introduced handles of Western Chou type, which clash with the rest. It is not the archaic motif as such that claims our attention, for archaisms occur earlier, as noted by Karlgren on various occasions. The point is that in the present instance we are faced with an unmitigated contrast of an extremely advanced or "modern" décor style with the antique element of the handles, which are associated with the modern décor regardless of stylistic or aesthetic unity. These handles are a direct quotation, as it were, from early Western Chou, showing not only an intense concern with that distant period but also the late bronze master's unquestionable knowledge of authentic ancient forms.

75 LID WITH SILVER INLAY
Late Eastern Chou
DIAM. 4⅞ in.
Nelson-Atkins Gallery of Art, Kansas City, Mo. (Nelson Fund)

The slightly convex surface of this circular lid with a movable ring in the center is covered with a magnificently designed repeat pattern of vortical construction. The pattern consists of intertwined, curvilinear bands in very intricate configurations. Three of these bands, shaped like large, mirror-reversed C's, cut across the other bands in more or less concentric position and provide the clearest orientation for the three repeating units. For the most part these bands are formed by a wider strip in the middle and thin lines on both sides; however, single, thin lines do run between and "under" them, as do also a few bands made up of two strands only. Here and there, bands merge, forming widened areas of varied shapes. Marked by either concentric circles alone or concentric circles in eye-like contours, either of which read as eyes, the widened areas suggest, however vaguely, zoomorphous heads. This does not mean that the designs should be interpreted as "dissolved dragons" or any kind of "corrupted" animal image. Perhaps the concentric circles were inserted for purely formal reasons or as a matter of fashion; they remain trivial details in the total plan of the pattern, which remains fundamentally geometric.

Published: Nelson-Atkins Gallery *Handbook*, 3rd ed., p. 131.

For a brief discussion of the relative date as compared with the lid from Seattle, the reader is referred to No. 76.

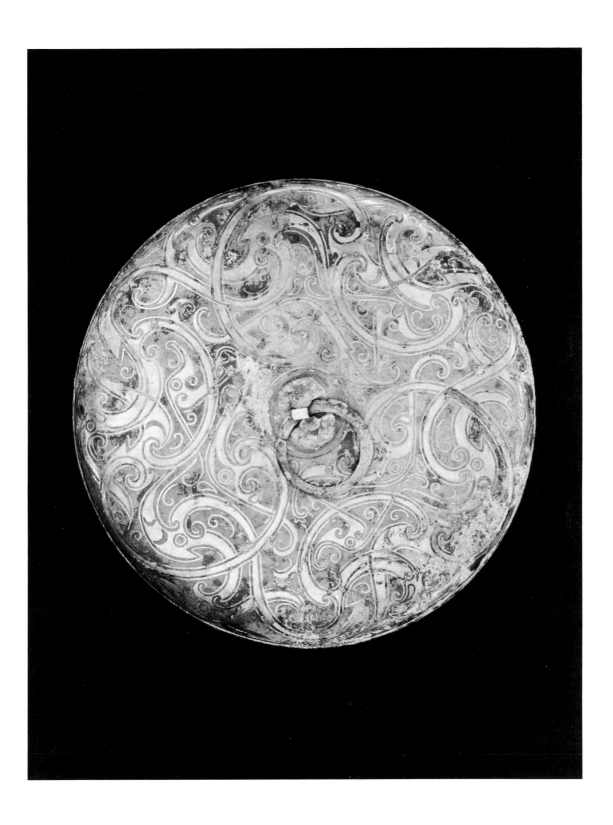

76   LID WITH SILVER INLAY
Late Eastern Chou
DIAM. 4⅜ in.
Seattle Art Museum; Eugene Fuller Memorial Collection

The surface of this flattish, convex lid, to the center of which a lug is affixed, is covered by a repeat pattern of complicated, curvilinear ornaments. Though organized much on the same principle as the design on the lid No. 75, the forms cohere in larger figures, reading as such; in fact, each of the three sectors is dominated by one continuous figure that occupies the entire arc. These large figures, moreover, are quite clearly distinguished from the thin-line curls and figures filling the spaces between the large ones. On the whole, therefore, the design is not composed primarily of individually distinct bands of fairly even width, but of flamboyant, curvilinear figures, large and small. The zoomorphous aspect given to some or, indeed, most of the ornaments is far more pronounced than in the case of the Kansas City specimen. Eyes, both circular and angular, are readily discerned. The angular eyes belong to the large figures, which hence assume the character of "dragon" figures; the forms surrounding the eyes do in fact resemble or, at least, remind one of ancient dragon heads. It seems fairly certain that these forms allude to archaic forms, and that they represent an archaistic element within a design quite unlike ancient designs. This kind of archaism is quite different from the wholesale borrowing we have seen in the handles of Western Chou type attached to the late Eastern Chou *Tui* of the Musée Guimet, No. 74.

Published: Seattle Art Museum, *Handbook*, 1951, p. 47; *Engagement Book*, 1962, opp. February 18; Portland Art Museum, *Gift to a City*, 1965, Cat. No. 11; Bunker, *The Art of Eastern Chou*, Cat. No. 38; Loehr, *Chinese Art: Symbols and Images*, Wellesley College, 1967, Cat. No. 8.

The two small lids, Nos. 75 and 76, are works of surpassing elegance and precision. Unfortunately their historical position is quite insufficiently known. Conceivably the Kansas City lid is the older of the two. It is difficult, of course, to compare their circular compositions with decorations adapted to horizontal friezes or rectangular walls, but it is possible that the design of the Victoria & Albert *Fang Hu*, No. 71, would stylistically fall between the two lids.

The small, thin-line figures of No. 76 compare quite well with the main décor of a *Tui* in the Freer Gallery (*Freer Gallery Bronzes*, pl. 33), a vessel of the type of the Musée Guimet *Tui*, No. 74 above, but with mask-and-ring handles instead of the outrageous Western Chou loop handles of the latter. The décor in question presents us with a delicate, silver inlay design of symmetrically paired birds strongly reminiscent of Western Chou bird images, but executed in double outlines and freely applied curls and spirals both within and without the paired birds. By virtue of the approximate date, the inlay technique, the same kind of lineament, and the same kind of archaisms in the lid No. 76 from Seattle it would seem safe to recognize a connection with the Freer Gallery vessel. Parenthetically, it may be noted that the motif in the border zones of the Freer *Tui* (diagonals crossed by curving bands which issue from, and end at, concentric circlets) is rather similar to the motif in the foot panel of the Victoria & Albert *Fang Hu*, No. 71.

77 CHARIOT FITTING
Late Eastern Chou
L. 7¾ in., w. 3¼ in.
Mr. and Mrs. A. B. Martin (Guennol Collection); courtesy of The Brooklyn Museum

A long, tapering, upward-bent hook, terminating in an animal head, projects from the inward-curved front of a rectangular socket. Save for the inward-curved part, the surface is decorated with symmetrically arranged geometric patterns, spirals, and scalloped curves inlaid in silver. Formerly in the J. Homberg collection, Paris, it is one of a pair.

Published: Bunker, *The Art of Eastern Chou*, Cat. No. 18.

Finials of this type are reported by W. C. White to have been found at Chin-ts'un (*Tombs of Old Lo-yang*, Nos. 051, 052). White mentions that in the *Po-ku-t'u* this type of object is "stated to have been a part of a royal chariot" (*ibid.*, p. 70). Comparable material is recorded in Umehara, *Rakuyō Kinson*, rev. ed., pls. 72–76; Kelley and Ch'en, *Buckingham Bronzes*, pl. 61; Karlgren, "Hellström Collection," pl. 39:4; d'Argencé, *Brundage Bronzes*, pl. 49:B. As regards the ornamentation of No. 77, it is to the Brundage specimen, a piece of exceptional refinement, that it compares most closely.

78 RING WITH SILVER INLAY
Late Eastern Chou
DIAM. 4⅞ in.
Mr. and Mrs. A. B. Martin (Guennol Collection); courtesy of The Brooklyn Museum

An object of utmost simplicity, this ring is transformed by its chaste and tranquil geometric ornamentation into a work of expressive form—lucid and serene. The ornaments are done in silver inlay, and there are three factors that combine to produce their particular effect. First, the silver bands are, on the whole, of equal width; there is no dynamic quality or restlessness in them. Second, bronze surfaces and silver surfaces are in ideal balance; the silver is not skimpy, and the bronze is not disregarded but remains essential to the design. Third, and perhaps most important, is the fact that the décor is arranged crosswise, in four repeats, so that the motifs, in themselves restrained and quiet, are steadied throughout. In this static setting the spirals, too, seem inactive. According to Bunker's catalogue entry, the back is slightly concave and undecorated. The ring was formerly in the collection of J. Homberg, Paris.

Published: Bunker, *The Art of Eastern Chou*, Cat. No. 30.

In addition to being simple, the ring described above is a rarity. Among the many Chin-ts'un finds recorded by White there is only one item to compare, a disk with sharp outer edge decorated with gold and silver inlay, flawless but conventional, and possessing nothing of the exquisite properties of No. 78 (White, *Tombs of Old Lo-yang*, pl. 5: 010 a,b).

79 BRONZE TUBE WITH SILVER INLAY
Han Period
H. 9¹³⁄₃₂ in., DIAM. 2½ in.
City Art Museum of Saint Louis

A cylindrical tube with a concave, splayed rim at one of the open ends is girdled by a roll in the middle. The surface is decorated all over with a silver inlaid design of great complexity. Part of the inlay is missing, so that the patterns seem more irregular now than they were originally. They are composed symmetrically at both sides of vertical axes, but at the same time are divided into horizontal zones. Within this rigid system, however, the forms of the ornaments vary, from zone to zone, in ever new combinations, and diagonally placed forms cut freely across the horizontal divisions. Scattered between the larger forms of silver sheet, that have been applied in inexplicable contours, are small dotted rosettes, concentric circles, slender drops, and many starlets. These compete actively with the innumerable finely drawn spirals which issue from the tips and points and corners of the larger forms.

Published: Kidder, *Early Chinese Bronzes*, pl. 29, left.

A comparable inlaid tube of about the same size is in the British Museum (Yetts, *Eumorfopoulos Catalogue*, I, A99 and 100); another, less than half its length, is in the Seligman Collection (Hansford, *The Seligman Collection*, pl. 26:A52). Drawings of two such tubes in the *Ning-shou chien-ku* (ch. 14:19, 20) show the layout of the design both in zones and in vertical symmetry very clearly but, rendered in outline only, fail to bring out the contrast of silver and bronze areas. All these objects conform to the same basic scheme of ornamentation, employing the same motifs. The character of these ornaments differs widely from that of the inlay patterns seen above (Nos. 71–78). It is very unlikely, therefore, that this group of tubes would be contemporaneous with any of them. The tubes are no doubt later than the objects decorated with sweeping bands and swirling scrolls, among which the *Tui* of the Musée Guimet, No. 74, may be the latest. A Han date seems the earliest possible one; Hansford, in fact, considers a post-Han date.

80   LIEN
Han Period
H. 8⅝ in., W. (including handles) 9½ in.
Staatliches Museum für Völkerkunde, Munich

This round box with two mask-and-ring handles, on three short, modeled feet, is covered with a convex lid, the flattened top of which is adorned by a plain quatrefoil in low relief. A loop holding a movable ring is attached to the center of the quatrefoil. On the circular frame surrounding the flower stand three short, rounded stumps that serve as feet when the lid is turned over. The edges of the lid and the box are strengthened and unobtrusively emphasized by plain bands. A similar band circling the middle of the box is further accentuated by a roll. Save for the masks and the simple quatrefoil on the cover, the vessel's surface is plain.

Not previously published.

Unadorned vessels probably were the rule rather than exceptions in high antiquity, instances being Nos. 1, 10, 11, 16. In this late phase, plainness and simplicity have an unnaive, deliberate quality about them. The absence of ornament intensifies the air of frugality resulting from the neat, sparing, and functional design of the vessel and its parts, among which the short stumps on the cover are the most conspicuous.

In the Eastern Han tomb of Wang Kuang, who was a secretary to the Governor of Lo-lang, Korea, a very similar but ornate lacquer *lien* or toilet box with the same short stumps on its lid was found; see T. Oba and K. Kayamoto, *The Tomb of Wang Kuang of Lo-lang*, Seoul, 1935, pls. 61, 62; also Umehara and Fujita, *Chōsen kobunka sōkan*, II, Tamba and Kyoto, 1948, pl. 22. Another tomb of the Lo-lang period, Sekiganri No. 9, which, by reason of two lacquer trays dated Chü-she 3rd year (A.D. 8) contained in it, is more precisely datable, yielded two bronze objects that may be compared with the box from Munich. One is a taller *Lien* with a chained bracket handle. It, too, is plain, with the same band and roll around the middle of the body and with exactly the same kind of short, modeled feet. The other is a box like No. 80, but with recumbent animals (tigers?) as supports and recumbent rams on the lid; see Umehara and Fujita, *op. cit.*, pls. 5, 6. The latter type, supported by standing beasts, is represented in Dr. Wessén's collection, Stockholm; see Karlgren, "Wessén Collection," pls. 29, 30.

No. 7: view from above.

No. 11, Ho

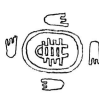

No. 13, Ku

No. 14, Chia

No. 16, Yu

No. 21, Li-Ting

No. 28, P'an

No. 31, Fang Chia

No. 36, Yü

No. 38, Fang I

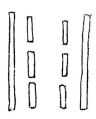

No. 40, Yu

No. 43, Lei

No. 47, Tsun

No. 48, Kuei

No. 49, Kuei

No. 53, Li

No. 50, Kuang

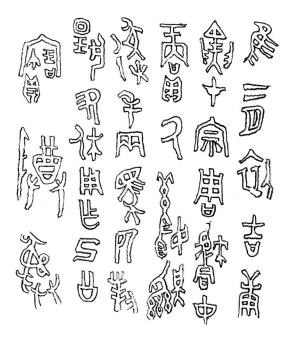

No. 54, FANG TING

No. 56, FANG I

No. 59, HU

No. 55, FANG TING

SELECTED BIBLIOGRAPHY

Abbreviated Titles of Periodicals:

AA	Artibus Asiae
ACASA	Archives of the Chinese Art Society of America
BAS	Bulletin, Institute of History and Philology, Academia Sinica
BMFEA	Bulletin, Museum of Far Eastern Antiquities
JRAS	Journal of the Royal Asiatic Society
KKHP	K'ao-ku Hsüeh-pao, "The Chinese Journal of Archaeology"
OA	Oriental Art
OZ	Ostasiatische Zeitschrift
TOCS	Transactions, Oriental Ceramic Society

Ackerman, Phyllis. *Ritual Bronzes of Ancient China*. New York: 1945.

Andersson, Johann Gunnar. "The Goldsmith in Ancient China," *BMFEA*, VII (1935).

Archaeology in New China (Hsin Chung-kuo ti k'ao-ku shou-huo). (Archaeol. Monograph Ser. A, Vol. VI, 1962.) Peking: The Institute of Archaeology, Academia Sinica.

Bachhofer, Ludwig. "The Evolution of Shang and Early Chou Bronzes," *The Art Bulletin*, June, 1944.

———. *A Short History of Chinese Art*. New York: 1946.

Barnard, Noel. *Bronze Casting and Bronze Alloys in Ancient China*. (Monumenta Serica Monograph, XIV, 1961.)

Bunker, Emma. *The Art of Eastern Chou*. Catalogue of a loan Exhibition at China House, Nov.–Dec., 1962. New York: Chinese Art Society of America, 1962.

Ch'en Meng-chia. "Style of Chinese Bronzes," *ACASA*, I (1946).

———. "Chronology of Western Chou Bronzes" (Hsi Chou t'ung-ch'i tuan-tai), *KKHP*, IX–XIV (1955–56).

Cheng-sung-t'ang chi-ku i-wen, 16 ch., pu-i, 3 ch., hsü-pien, 3 ch., by Lo Chen-yü, 1931.

Ch'eng-tzu-yai. (*Archaeologia Sinica*, No. 1, 1934.) Nanking: The Institute of History and Philology, Academia Sinica.

Cheng-chou Erh-li-kang. (Archaeol. Monograph Ser. D., Vol. VII, 1959.) Peking: The Institute of Archaeology, Academia Sinica.

Chêng Tê-k'un, *Archaeology in China*, Vol. II: *Shang China*. Toronto: 1960. Vol. III: *Chou China*. Cambridge and Toronto: 1963.

Consten, Eleanor von Erdberg. "A Terminology of Chinese Bronze Decoration," *Monumenta Serica*, XVI/1–2 (1957); XVII (1958).

———. *Das alte China*. Stuttgart: 1958.

Creel, Herlee Glessner. "On the Origins of the Manufacture and Decoration of Bronze in the Shang Period," *Monumenta Serica*, I (1935).

———. "Notes on Prof. Karlgren's System for Dating Chinese Bronzes," *JRAS*, July, 1936.

Davidson, J. Leroy. "Toward a Grouping of Early Chinese Bronzes," *Parnassus*, Pt. 1, IX/4 (1937); Pt. 2, X/1 (1938).

Dewall, Magdalene von. "New Data on Early Chou Finds. Their Relative Chronology in Historical Perspective," *Symposium in honor of Dr. Li Chi*, Pt. II. Taipei: 1966.

Dubs, Homer H. "The Date of the Shang Period," *T'oung Pao*, XL/4–5 (1951); XLII/1–2 (1953).

Ecke, Gustav. *Frühe chinesische Bronzen aus der Sammlung Trautmann*. Peking: 1939.

———. *Sammlung Lochow: Chinesische Bronzen, I*. Peking: 1943.

Fairbank, Wilma. "Piece-mold Craftsmanship and Shang Bronze Design," *ACASA*, XVI (1962).

Feng-hsi fa-chüeh pao-kao (Report on Excavations at Feng-hsi). (Archaeol. Monograph Ser. D., Vol. XII, 1962) Peking: The Institute of Archaeology, Academia Sinica.

Ferguson, John C. *Li-tai chu-lu chi-chin-mu (Catalogue of the Recorded Bronzes of Successive Dynasties)*. Shanghai: 1939.

Freer Gallery Bronzes, A Descriptive and Illustrative Catalogue of Chinese Bronzes acquired during the administration of John Ellerton Lodge. Compiled by the Staff of the Freer Gallery of Art (J. E. Lodge, A. G. Wenley, J. A. Pope). (Freer Gallery of Art Oriental Studies, No. 3.) Washington: Smithsonian Institution, 1946.

Garner, Sir Harry. "The Composition of Chinese Bronzes," *OA*, VI/4 (Winter, 1960).

Grassl, Catherine. "New Researches on Chinese Bronzes," *The Art Bulletin*, March, 1943.

Gyllensvärd, Bo. "Floral Pattern in Early Chinese Bronzes," *BMFEA*, XXXIV (1962).

Hakkaku kikkinshū (Chinese Bronzes in the Hakuzuru Museum). Hyōgo: 1934.

Hansford, Sidney Howard. *The Seligman Collection of Oriental Art*, Vol. I. London: 1957.

———. "Pre-Anyang," *OA*, IV/1 (Spring, 1958).

Higuchi, Takayasu, "Sei-Shū dōki no kenkyū" ("A New Study on Western Chou Bronzes"), *Kyōto Daigaku Bungaku-bu Kenkyū Kiyō*, VII (1963).

Ho-nan chi-chin t'u-chih sheng-kao, by Sun Hai-po, 1940.

HPKM 1001: see *Liang Ssu-yung*.

Hsün-hsien Hsin-ts'un, by Kuo Pao-chün. (Archaeol. Monograph Ser. B, Vol. XIII, 1964.) Peking: The Institute of Archaeology, Academia Sinica.

Hui-hsien fa-chüeh pao-kao. (Reports on Chinese Field Archaeology, Vol. I, 1956.) Peking: The Institute of Archaeology, Academia Sinica.

"In-dai seidō-bunka no kenkyū" ("Studies of the bronze culture of the Yin period"). A symposium with contributions by S. Kaizuka, M. Ito, S. Mizuno, T. Okazaki, et al. *Tōhō Gakuhō*, XXIII (1953).

Jakobsen, Kristian. "Chinesische Bronzen," *Jahrbuch der Hamburger Kunstsammlungen*, IV. Hamburg: 1959.

Jenyns, R. Soame, and Watson, William. *Chinese Art*, Vol. II: *The Minor Arts; Gold, Silver, Bronze, etc.* London and New York: 1963.

Jung Keng. *Shang Chou i-ch'i t'ung-k'ao*, 2 vols. Peking: 1941.

———. *Yin Chou ch'ing-t'ung-ch'i t'ung-lun*. (Archaeol. Monograph Ser. C, Vol. II, 1958.) Peking: Institute of Archaeology, Academia Sinica.

Kao Ch'ü-hsün. "Problems of the Bronze Mirror discovered from a Shang Burial," *BAS*, XXIX (1958). (Cf. S. Umehara, "Chūgoku In-Shū no kogyō," *Shirin*, 1959/4, pp. 467–479).

Karlgren, Bernhard. "Yin and Chou in Chinese Bronzes," *BMFEA*, VIII (1936).

———. "The Dating of Chinese Bronzes," *JRAS* (1937), pp. 33–39.

———. "New Studies on Chinese Bronzes," *BMFEA*, IX (1937).

———. "Notes on a Kin-ts'un Album," *BMFEA*, X (1938).

———. "Once again the A and B Styles in Yin Ornamentation," *BMFEA*, XVIII (1946).

———. "Bronzes in the Hellström Collection," *BMFEA*, XX (1948).

———. "Some Bronzes in the Museum of Far Eastern Antiquities," *BMFEA*, XXI (1949).

———. "Notes on the Grammar of Early Bronze Décor," *BMFEA*, XXIII (1951).

———. *A Catalogue of the Chinese Bronzes in the Alfred F. Pillsbury Collection*. Minneapolis: The Minneapolis Institute of Arts, 1952.

———. "Bronzes in the Wessén Collection," *BMFEA*, XXX (1958).

———. "Marginalia on Some Bronze Albums," *BMFEA*, XXXI (1959); XXXII (1960).

———. "Some Characteristics of Yin Art," *BMFEA*, XXXIV (1962).

Kelley, Charles Fabens, and Ch'en Meng-chia. *Chinese Bronzes from the Buckingham Collection*. Chicago: The Art Institute of Chicago, 1946.

Kidder, Jonathan Edward, Jr. *Early Chinese Bronzes in the City Art Museum of St. Louis*. St. Louis: 1956.

Ku Kung t'ung-ch'i t'u-lu. Compiled by the Joint Administration of the National Palace and Central Museums. 2 vols. Taipei: 1958.

Kümmel, Otto. *Chinesische Bronzen aus der Abteilung für Ostasiatische Kunst an den Staatlichen Museen Berlin*. Berlin, 1928.

Kuo Mo-jo. *Liang Chou chin-wen-tz'u ta-hsi t'u-lu k'ao-shih*. Tokyo: 1935. Second edition, Peking: 1958.

Kuo Pao-chün, "Report on the Excavations at Yin-hsü in the Spring of 1950," *KKHP*, V (1951).

La Plante, John D. *Arts of the Chou Dynasty*. Catalogue of an exhibition at Stanford University Museum, Feb.–March, 1958. Stanford: 1958.

Lefebvre d'Argencé, René-Yvon. *Ancient Chinese Bronzes in the Avery Brundage Collection*. San Francisco: de Young Museum Society and Diablo Press, 1966.

Leth, André. *A Selection of the Exhibits shown at the Museum of Decorative Arts, Copenhagen, 1950*. Copenhagen: NYT Nordisk Forlag, 1953.

Li Chi, "Chi Hsiao-t'un ch'u-t'u chih ch'ing-t'ung-ch'i," *KKHP*, III (1948); IV (1949).

———. "Diverse Backgrounds of the Decorative Art of the Yin Dynasty," *Annals of the Academia Sinica*, No. II, Pt. 1 (1955), pp. 119–129.

———. *The Beginnings of Chinese Civilization*. Three Lectures Illustrated with Finds at An-yang. Seattle: 1957.

———. "Studies of the Decorative Art of the Yin-Shang Period, Pt. 1." *BAS*, XXXIV (in memory of Dr. Hu Shih), Pt. II (1963).

Li Chi and Wan Chia-pao, *Studies of the Bronze Ku-Beaker*. (*Archaeologia Sinica*, N.S., No. 1.) Nankang, Taiwan: Academia Sinica, 1964.

———. *Studies of the Bronze Chüeh-Cup*. (*Archaeologia Sinica*, N.S., No. 2.) Nankang: Academia Sinica, 1966.

Liang Ssu-yung and Kao Ch'ü-hsün. *Hou Chia Chuang: HPKM 1001*; Pt. 1, Text; Pt. 2, Plates. (*Archaeologia Sinica*, No. 3, Vol. II.) Taipei: Academia Sinica, 1962.

Lippe, Aschwin. "A Gift of Chinese Bronzes," *The Metropolitan Museum of Art Bulletin*, IX/4 (December, 1950).

Lochow, Hans Juergen von. *Sammlung Lochow: Chinesische Bronzen, II*. Peking: 1944.

Loehr, Max. "Bronzentexte der Chou-Zeit. Chou I (1)," *Sinologische Arbeiten*, II (1944), Peking; continuation, "Chou I (2)," *Monumenta Serica*, XI (1946).

———. "The Bronze Styles of the Anyang Period," *ACASA*, VII (1953).

———. *Chinese Bronze Age Weapons*. The Werner Jannings

Collection in the Chinese National Palace Museum, Peking. Ann Arbor: The University of Michigan Press, 1956.

———. *Relics of Ancient China, from the Collection of Dr. Paul Singer*. Catalogue of a loan exhibition at Asia House, Jan.–March, 1965. New York: The Asia Society, 1965.

Lo-yang Chung-chou-lu. (Archaeol. Monograph Ser. D, Vol. IV, 1959.) Peking: The Institute of Archaeology, Academia Sinica.

Lo-yang Shao-kou Han-mu. (Archaeol. Monograph Ser. D, Vol. VI, 1959.) Peking: The Institute of Archaeology, Academia Sinica.

Ma Te-chih, et al. "Report on Excavations at Ta-ssu-k'ung-ts'un, An-yang, 1953," *KKHP*, IX (1955), pp. 25–90.

Miao-ti-kou yü San-li-ch'iao. (Archaeol. Monograph Ser. D, Vol. IX, 1959.) Peking: The Institute of Archaeology, Academia Sinica.

Mizuno, Seiichi. *Bronzes and Jades of Ancient China*. Tokyo: The Nihon Keizai, 1959.

———. "Ancient Chinese Bronzes and Jades," *OA*, V/4 (Winter, 1959), pp. 132–155.

Ning-shou chien-ku, 16 ch. Peking: 1913.

Pelliot, Paul. "The Royal Tombs of Anyang," in *Studies in Chinese Art and Some Indian Influences*, by J. Hackin, et al. London: 1938.

Senoku Seishō (The Collection of Old Bronzes of K. Sumitomo). New and rev. ed., by K. Hamada and S. Umehara. Kyoto: 1934. *New Acquisitions*, by S. Umehara, 1961.

Shan-chai chi-chin-lu, 28 ts'e, by Liu T'i-chih. Shanghai: 1934.

Shan-chai i-ch'i t'u-lu, 3 ts'e, by Jung Keng. Peking: 1936.

Shan-piao-chen yü Liu-li-ko, by Kuo Pao-chün. (Archaeol. Monograph, Ser. B, Vol. XI, 1959.) Peking: The Institute of Archaeology, Academia Sinica.

Shanghai Museum Bronzes (Shang-hai Po-wu-kuan ts'ang ch'ing-t'ung-ch'i). 2 vols. Shanghai: 1964.

Shang-ts'un-ling Kuo-kuo mu-ti (The Cemetery of the State of Kuo at Shang-ts'un-ling). Archaeological Excavations at the Yellow River Reservoirs Report No. 3. (Archaeol. Monograph Ser. D, Vol. X, 1959.) Peking: The Institute of Archaeology, Academia Sinica.

Shih Chang-ju. "Bronze Casting in the Shang Dynasty," *BAS*, XXVI (1955).

———. "Kneeling Burials at the Yin-Shang Sites, Hsiao-t'un, An-yang," *BAS*, XXXVI (Tung Tso-pin Memorial Volume), Pt. 1 (1965).

Shou-hsien Ts'ai-hou mu ch'u-t'u i-wu (Objects excavated from the tomb of the Marquis of Ts'ai in Shou-hsien). (Archaeol. Monograph Ser. B, Vol. V, 1956.) Peking: The Institute of Archaeology, Academia Sinica.

Singer, Paul. "Pre-Dynastic and Dynastic Shang Material," *OA*, VI/2 (Summer, 1960).

———. "Postscript," *OA*, VI/3 (Autumn, 1960).

Soper, Alexander C. "The Tomb of the Marquis of Ts'ai," *OA*, X/3 (Autumn, 1964).

———. "Early, Middle, and Late Shang: A Note," *AA*, XXVIII (1966).

Stephen, Barbara. "Early Chinese Bronzes in the Royal Ontario Museum," *OA*, VIII/2 (Summer, 1962).

Sung-chai chi-chin t'u-lu, 2 ts'e, *hsü-lu*, 1 ts'e, by Jung Keng. Peking: 1933, 1938.

T'an Tan-chiung. *Chung-kuo t'ung-ch'i hua-wen chi (Decorative Patterns on Chinese Bronzes)*. Taipei: 1959.

Trübner, Jörg. *Yu und Kuang. Zur Typologie der chinesischen Bronzen*. Leipzig: 1929.

Tsun-ku-chai so-chien chi-chin-t'u, 4 ch., by Huang Chün. Peking: 1936.

Umehara, Sueji. *Seika = Ōbei shūchō Shina kodō seika (Selected Relics of Ancient Chinese Bronzes from Collections in Europe and America)*. 7 vols. Osaka: 1933.

———. *Henkin no kōkogaku-teki kōsatsu (Etude archéologique sur le Pien-chin, ou série de bronzes avec une table pour l'usage rituel dans la Chine antique)*. (*Memoir*, Tōhō Bunka Gakuin, Kyōto Kenkyūjo, Vol. II.) Kyoto: 1933.

———. *Sengoku-shiki dōki no kenkyū (Etude des bronzes des Royaumes Combattants)*. Kyoto: 1936.

———. *Kanan Anyō ihō (Selected Ancient Treasures Found at Anyang, Yin Sites)*. Kyoto: 1940.

———. *Kodōki keitai no kōkogaku-teki kenkyū (On the Shapes of the Bronze Vessels of Ancient China: An Archaeological Study)*. (*Memoir*, Tōhō Bunka Kenkyūjo, Vol. XV.) Kyoto: 1940.

———. *Kanan Anyō ibutsu no kenkyū (A Study of Relics from Anyang, Honan)*. Kyoto: 1941.

———. *Seizansō Seishō, Kodōki-hen (Illustrated Catalogue of the K. Nezu Collection, Volume on Ancient Bronzes)*. Tokyo: 1942.

———. *Rakuyō Kinson kobo shuei (Selection of tomb finds from Lo-yang Chin-ts'un)*. Kyoto: 1937; rev. ed., 1944.

———. "Sensei-shō Hōkeiken shutsudo no dai ni no henkin" ("The Second Set of Ritual Vessels, Pien-chin, from Pao-chi-hsien, Shensi Province"), *Tōhōgaku Kiyō*, I (1959). With an English Summary.

———. *Nihon Seika = Nihon shūcho Shina kodō seika (A Selection of Ancient Chinese Bronzes in Japanese Collections)*. 6 vols. Osaka: 1961.

———. *Inkyo (Yin Hsu, Ancient Capital of the Shang Dynasty at An-yang)*. Tokyo: 1964.

Waterbury, Florance. *Early Chinese Symbols and Literature: Vestiges and Speculations*. With particular reference to the Ritual Bronzes of the Shang Dynasty. New York: 1942.

Watson, William. *Archaeology in China*. London: 1961.

———. *China before the Han Dynasty*. London: 1961.

———. *Ancient Chinese Bronzes*. Rutland, Vermont: 1962.

———. *Handbook to the Collections of Early Chinese Antiquities*. London: The Trustees of the British Museum, 1963.

Weber, Charles D. "Chinese Pictorial Bronze Vessels of the Late Chou Period," Pt. I, *AA*, XXVIII/2–3 (1966); Pt. II, *AA*, XXVIII/4 (1966); Pt. III, *AA*, XXIX/2–3 (1967).

White, William Charles. *Tombs of Old Lo-yang*. Shanghai: 1934.

———. *Bronze Culture of Ancient China*. An Archaeological Study of Bronze Objects from Northern Honan, dating from about 1400 B.C. to 771 B.C. (Royal Ontario Museum of Archaeology, Museum Studies, No. V.) Toronto: 1956.

Wu-ying-tien i-ch'i t'u-lu, 2 ts'e, by Jung Keng. Peking: 1934.

Yang Shu-ta. *Chi-wei-chü chin-wen shuo*. (Archaeol. Monograph Ser. A, Vol. I, 1952; enlarged and rev. ed., 1959.) Peking: The Institute of Archaeology, Academia Sinica.

Yeh-chung p'ien-yü, Pts. I, II, III, by Huang Chün. Peking: 1935, 1937, 1942.

Yen-k'u chi-chin t'u-lu, 2 ch., by Liang Shang-ch'un. Peking: 1944.

Yetts, W. Perceval. *The George Eumorfopoulos Collection: Catalogue of the Chinese and Korean Bronzes, Sculpture, Jade, Jewellery and Miscellaneous Objects*. 3 vols. London: 1929–1932.

———. *The Cull Chinese Bronzes*. London: University of London, Courtauld Institute of Art, 1939.

Young, Jean Johnson. *Small Sculpture, Shang through Sung Dynasties*. Catalogue of a loan Exhibition at China House, Feb.–April, 1954. New York: Chinese Art Society of America, 1954.

———. *Art Styles of Ancient Shang, from Private and Museum Collections*. Catalogue of a loan exhibition at China House, April–June, 1967. New York: China Institute in America, 1967.

Catalogue designed and edited by Virginia Field, Assistant Director, Asia House Gallery.

Color photographs Nos. 3 and 52 are by Otto E. Nelson; No. 20 is by D. C. Millard;
No. 41 is by John McQuade; No. 72 is by Richard Brittain.

The following black and white photographs are by Otto E. Nelson:
8, 15, 17, 22, 24, 42, 44, 50, 58, 60, 64, 66, 73.

Color engravings made by Brüder Hartmann, Berlin.

Black and white illustrations by The Meriden Gravure Company, Meriden, Conn.

Printed and bound by Clarke & Way, Inc., New York.